Early American
METAL PROJECTS

Early American
METAL PROJECTS

JOSEPH WILLIAM DANIELE

Department Chairman
Metal and Technical Drawing Department
Ludlow High School
Ludlow, Massachusetts

McKNIGHT & McKNIGHT PUBLISHING COMPANY
Bloomington, Illinois

To Jean,

My Co-author

Her gentle persistence and guidance were always welcome;

but her unselfish assistance was my real asset.

Preface

In presenting a historical background to the projects in this book, I hope to renew a sense of pride in the accomplishments of our inventive American forefathers and inspire an awareness of the timelessness of colonial design. Settlers were ingenious as they used their own hands to make the things needed for everyday life in the new land. These artifacts are now regarded as remarkable and valued memorabilia of our rich history.

Compared to many countries whose histories may span two thousand or more years, the heritage we draw from is relatively short. Nevertheless, the American past is full of courageous men and women who battled the fierceness of nature, Indians, and Englishmen. These same people who shaped a nation out of a wilderness on a dream of freedom, independence, and human rights also created household necessities of grace, charm, and fine workmanship.

It is the work of these illustrious pioneers that I seek to emulate in the projects presented here. Each reproduction represents colonial America; each one speaks of the past, transcending the lapse of time and reuniting modern man with his 17th-century ancestors.

Americans can take pride in their heritage. To that end these reproductions are dedicated.

Joseph William Daniele

Acknowledgments

Obtaining the general information and historical background for this book required the help of many people: some of them are associated with historical restorations, some own private collections, and some are just good friends. The author extends sincere thanks and appreciation to the following for their assistance:

John F. Albano, photographer

Antique Magazine

Circle F Industries

Colonial Williamsburg

Joseph Dixon Crucible Company

Essex Institute

Guilford Courthouse National Park

Industrial Arts and Vocational Education Magazine

Ludlow (Massachusetts) High School students

Metropolitan Museum of Art

Mystic Seaport

Byron Matthews & Newburyport Historical Society

Old Sturbridge Village

Pennsylvania Museum of Art

Pennsylvania Farm Museum of Landis County

Philadelphia Chamber of Commerce

Plymouth Plantation

Henry Salem

Shelbourne Museum Inc.

Smithsonian Institution

U.S. Military Academy at West Point

U.S. Department of Interior

Henry Francis duPont Winterthur Museum

Mr. and Mrs. Walter L. Wolf

Table of Contents

Introduction

Colonialism in design, decor, and construction is timeless. The warmth and character of colonial design is not found in either the intricate scrolls of the gothic period or the clinical, straight lines of contemporary times. Colonial furnishings suggest, perhaps, the determination, spirit, and adventurous nature of the early settlers. For a great many years, colonial decor was popular only in New England; in recent years, however, interest in the colonial theme has spread nationwide.

Many decorators claim that everything in a room or home, including the smallest item, should complement and accent the period of decor. Thus, in a colonial home all the accessories should be consistent and compatible with the overall furnishings.

Since many homeowners cannot afford to furnish their homes with costly antiques, they can make use of reproductions. The pieces or accessories presented as projects in this book enhance modern colonial settings. Students and home craftsmen can make candle sconces, lamps, firetools, or various iron and tin items which lend authenticity to colonial decor. Most of the projects are true to the original article, while the rest are composites of several colonial designs which have been developed into period pieces.

Colonial Wrought Iron

A brief history of each reproduction focuses on the interesting circumstances surrounding the colonist's use of the household item or how the item was developed to suit his needs. Some of these articles, such as the scoop sconce and the strap hinge sconce, were originally made from discarded utensils. Since metals were scarce in the new land, the colonist used great ingenuity in modifying old objects to suit new needs.

A picture of the authentic colonial piece is shown with the project whenever one is available so that the reproduction may be compared to the antique. In several of the pieces, the material of the original has been changed to make the article easier to construct in a school shop.

The early colonists had a very limited choice of manufacturing material. Much of the iron and all of the early tinplate was imported from England. The domestic pig iron made at Saugus and Hammersmith, Massachusetts, was very rough and crudely finished. Casting was often done on the dirt floor at the smelting mill with little concern about the finish. Nevertheless, the charm of colonial pieces made from such metal is in the design, and that aspect has been preserved in these projects.

The materials, sizes, and construction techniques are stated for each project, but they may be altered to meet individual desires, needs, and resources. Brass, bronze, aluminum, pewter, galvanized sheet metal, or opened tin cans are suitable basic stock for a great many of these projects.

Colonial Design

In colonial times, everything was handmade and, as such, became *one of a kind.* If a housewife needed a door latch or pair of hinges, she asked her husband to inform the village blacksmith of her needs. In due time the smith produced her order.

Although hinges, latches, or andirons were made to a particular order and size, design to a large extent was up to the blacksmith as he used his own ideas

and available material. Therefore, no two articles were ever exactly alike. As projects from this book are constructed, this thought of originality should be kept in mind. The student is free to use his own designs and ideas, but certain rules or concepts should be retained so that the reproduction is authentic in style. The following details which distinguish colonial design are not to be considered hard, fast rules, but rather guides to planning a satisfying reproduction. Many of the suggestions for construction have been developed by other students.

Pointing

Characteristic of early American metalwork was the *point,* an elongation of the ends of a piece. These points

Fig. 1-1.   Wrought Iron and Steel Door Handles of the 18th-19th Century (Metropolitan Museum of Art, Cadwalader Fund, 1918)

The distinguished shape of the ends of these handles provided not only beauty of design but also greater holding power.

(The Smithsonian Institution)

served a dual purpose: (1) they gave an artistic touch to articles used in otherwise austere surroundings, and (2) they permitted greater holding power in the case of hinges and handles. Figure 1-1 shows some authentic *colonial points* found on household hardware, and Fig. 1-2 shows some of the *common points* used in modern reproductions. Use of any of these points preserves the colonial concept in a design.

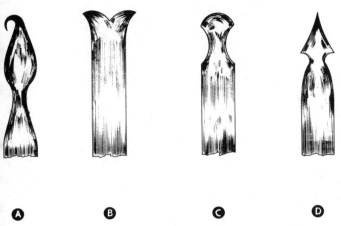

A   **B**   **C**   **D**

Fig. 1-2.   Common New England Points: (A) Rattail, (B) Fishtail, (C) Flair, (D) Spear

Fastening

Blacksmiths joined metals by *forge welding.* Two pieces of stock were heated until the white-hot iron gave off sparks. The two pieces were overlapped and hammered. Tinkers or whitesmiths employed both rivets and lead solder to fasten metals together. This is illustrated in Fig. 1-3 which shows how the sheet metal candle socket is riveted to wrought iron and the candle socket is soldered to the dish. While most authentic reproductions are made by these fastening methods, other means, such as threading, arc or spot welding, and

bolting, may be substituted. For truly authentic reproductions, fastening should be by riveting and soldering.

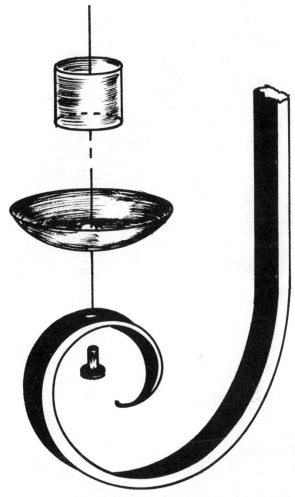

Fig. 1-3.   Fastening Detail for a Candle Socket and Drip Dish on a Wall Sconce

Design and Trim

Most early pieces were devoid of trim or borders. The real beauty of these articles is the perfect classical design and simplicity. About 1772 the American eagle became a symbol of freedom from English rule. As such, the eagle became an important part of early American design, Fig. 1-4. Second to the eagle as design choices were the colorful fruit, flower, and heart decoration introduced by the Pennsylvania Dutch. Much of this work is called *toleware*.

Fig. 1-4.   American Eagle Decorates Sternboard on the Charles W. Morgan (Marine Historical Assn., Inc., Mystic Seaport)
The design is applicable to many projects in early American reproductions.

Fig. 1-5.   Toleware (Shelburne Museum, Inc., E. J. Mengis)
Brightly colored designs introduced by the Pennsylvania Dutch appeared on tin utensils.

Finishing

Colonial artisans did little to give a protective finish to their work. This explains why a great many of their earliest products finally deteriorated. However, about 1734, *painted* or *japanned* objects appeared in the colonies. Some fine examples of painted tin pieces (toleware) are shown in Fig. 1-5. Thus, bright color does have a rightful place in colonial metalwork. Each project described in this book has a note on finishing which, at times, is a compromise between colonial and contemporary methods. They are only suggestions for completing the work.

Organization of Projects

Projects presented here are divided into units, each signifying a way of life in early America.

Unit 2 is devoted to candles and candle sconces — essential equipment in the colonial dwelling.

Unit 3 is concerned with fireplace equipment and tools, including andirons, firetools, trivets, and cranes.

Unit 4 centers around weapons, the tools of the revolution.

Unit 5 deals with an array of exterior metalwork, such as name signs, weather vanes, and lamps.

Unit 6 focuses on yankee tin and includes many examples of colonial tinwork made by the tinkers and whitesmiths.

Unit 7 includes plans on how to make authentic chandeliers and wall lamps. These plans answer the problems of modern colonial enthusiasts who seek satisfactory reproductions of early American lighting devices.

Unit 8 presents projects suitable for Christmas decoration. Although they are not authentic colonial reproductions since holiday decorating was unknown in those times, they are based upon pure colonial design.

Using the Appendix

The Appendix is an important aid in the use of this book. Basic information needed for successful reproduction of colonial projects is provided so that repetitious construction details, details of colonial design and so on are avoided; and the student can pursue his own creative efforts in proceeding with each project. Common sizes and types of stock are also listed.

The Appendix is divided into the following sections:

Section I explains the various design characteristics of colonial metalwork, such as forge points, scroll work and hammer marks, and how they are achieved; the construction of basic pieces, such as candle sockets and drip dishes; and making joints and seams to resemble the colonists' work.

Section II describes preparation of metal for finishing, degreasing metal, finishes appropriate to colonial reproductions, and suitable trims and designs.

Materials suggested for the projects have been standardized so that only a minimum number of stock varieties and sizes need be purchased for classroom use. *Section III* lists common stock sizes for metals used, fasteners and electrical equipment required, as well as suppliers of electrical parts and decal designs.

A great deal of research was undertaken to make these projects as authentic as possible. The Colonial Period, in general, lasted up until 1776 and the Early American Period until 1830. These two periods in history overlap, but they both incorporate a special heritage created by the spirit and resourcefulness of the people who left home and friends behind to seek a new life in America.

These craftsmen not only helped make a new world, but also created a period of design unequalled in any other era and gave us not only a heritage of freedom in government, but in design as well. Hopefully, the construction of reproductions in this book will recapture for the modern-day craftsman some of the feeling of freedom and pride in personal accomplishment enjoyed by the artisans of long ago.

UNIT 2

Candlelight

Early settlers had to rely on the fireplace, candles, or a torch made of pitch-pine splinters called *candlewood* for their supply of light. As the colonies were established, the lighting methods improved, and candles became the main source of illumination. Candlemaking required a great deal of time and was accomplished by dipping, Fig. 2-1, or using molds, Fig. 2-2.

The candleholder or *sconce* was a household necessity. Its unique construction protected the colonist's wood frame house from danger of fire. It also protected the flame from drafts. Tin was the logical choice of material for the sconce as well as for most household articles because the material was easy to form and was not plentiful.

A blacksmith or tinsmith made the sconces, but housewives decorated them, Fig. 2-7. The simplest sconces were formed with a scallop design hammered around the edges, Fig. 2-8. Subsequently, designs appeared in wider variety until sconcemaking became an art.

Early American enthusiasts find sconces attractive decoration for homes or such places of business as restaurants. They are attractive on tables or hung on walls. Reproductions in this unit are a comparatively easy beginning to colonial metalwork.

Fig. 2-1. The Dip Process of Candlemaking (Colonial Williamsburg)
Notice all the equipment necessary for this method of candlemaking.

Fig. 2-2. Candle Molds (Shelburne Museum, Inc., E. J. Mengis)

Scoop Sconce

The scoop sconce received its name from the economy-minded colonists who used old sugar and bean scoops (Fig. 2-3) for the basic construction. The high sides of the scoop were especially suited to protecting the lighted candle from drafts and confining the flame. This relieved somewhat the ever-present threat of fire in the colonists' wood shelters. The handle on the scoop (Fig. 2-4) permitted the sconce to be carried from room to room, as was common.

Materials

Although 26-gage stock is suggested, any other type of stock may be substituted. A tin can may be used to construct this sconce, but the sharp edges are a hazard. The entire scoop sconce is made from a piece of stock 12″ × 10″.

Fig. 2-3.   Sketch of an Early Tin Scoop Larger pieces were used as candle sconces.

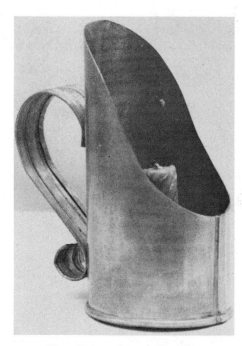

Fig. 2-4.   Scoop Sconce

Part	Pieces	Size	Suggested Material
A — Sides	1	8″ × 12″	26-gage sheet metal
B — Base	1	3 ½″ radius circle dia.	26-gage sheet metal
C — Handle	1	10″ × 1½″	26-gage sheet metal
Socket	1	¾″	26-gage sheet metal

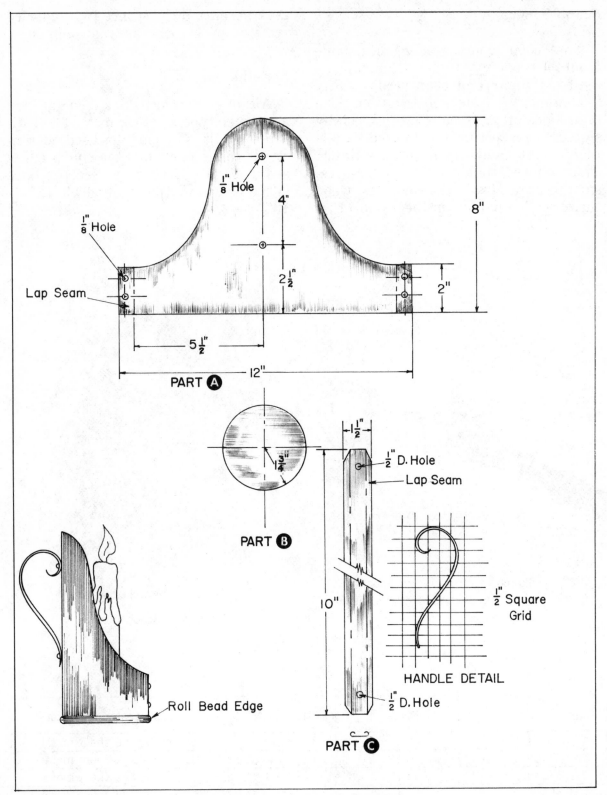

Fig. 2-5.   Project Views of Scoop Sconce

Construction Procedure

Lay out a full-size paper development (pattern) of parts *A*, *B*, and *C*, as shown in Fig. 2-5. Provide material for a ½" lap seam on both ends of parts *A* and hems on part *C*. Transfer the development to the sheet stock and cut the parts out.

Remove burrs from the edges with a file before forming the parts.

PART A — SIDES
Drill ⅛" holes for rivets.

Form part A into a cylindical shape (use a slip roll).

Make a roll bead edge on the lower circuference to receive part *B*. (use a rotary machine).

PART B — BASE
Fit part B into the bead edge on part *A*.

Rivet and solder part A to fit tightly around part *B*.

Solder a candle socket in the center of part *B*. (See Section I of the Appendix for the procedure in making a standard candle socket.)

PART C — HANDLE
Roll ¼" *edge or hem* of each side the entire length.

Shape the handle, following the general design for the scroll in Fig. 2-5. The handle should have 4" between fastening points to form a functional contour.

Drill ⅛" rivet holes in the high points of the handle.

Rivet the handle to part *A*.

Finish

The beauty of this piece is in its simplicity. The design is enhanced if the sconce is made of zinc-coated sheet metal which, when buffed with steel wool, takes on a sheen like Old English pewter. A brush or spray coating of clear lacquer will preserve the sheen of this buffed surface.

Another finish is a plain, flat black coat of paint. As a rule, the scoop sconce is devoid of any decoration or decal.

Wall Sconce

The distinguishing feature of the wall sconce is the high back. The high back, Figs. 2-6 and 2-8, protected the wall from the flame and served as a light reflector.

Some colonial housewives with artistic ability decorated this high back with a bird, a heart, or flower designs, Fig. 2-7. As these hand-painted sconces became popular, shopkeepers began to stock them. The painted tin was called *toleware*. Some innkeepers used the high back to post their rules of conduct where the guests were sure to see them, Fig. 2-9.

Fig. 2-7.   Wall Sconce Toleware
Decals are adequate substitutes for hand painting.

Fig. 2-6.   Single and Double Tin Candle Sconces Used by Pennsylvania Dutch (Philadelphia Museum of Art, Titus C. Greasey Collection)

Fig. 2-8.   Wall Sconce Is Made to Resemble Pewter and Decorated with Decal

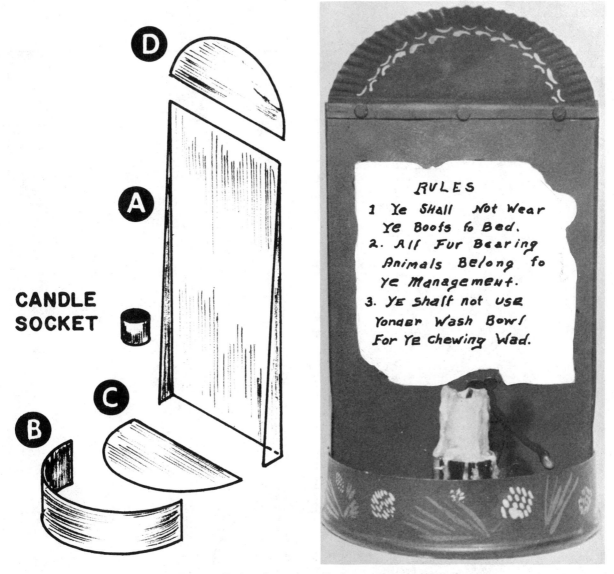

CANDLE
SOCKET

Fig. 2-9.　Tavern Rules Occasionally Appeared on Wall Sconces

Materials

Part	Pieces	Size	Suggested Material
A — Back	1	5'' × 10''	26-gage sheet metal (or tin, brass or pewter sheet stock)
B — Curved front	1	1 ½'' × 8''	26-gage sheet metal
C — Bottom	1	Semi-circle 2'' radius	26-gage sheet metal
D — Top	1	Semi-circle 2'' radius	26-gage sheet metal
Candle socket	1	¾''	26-gage sheet metal

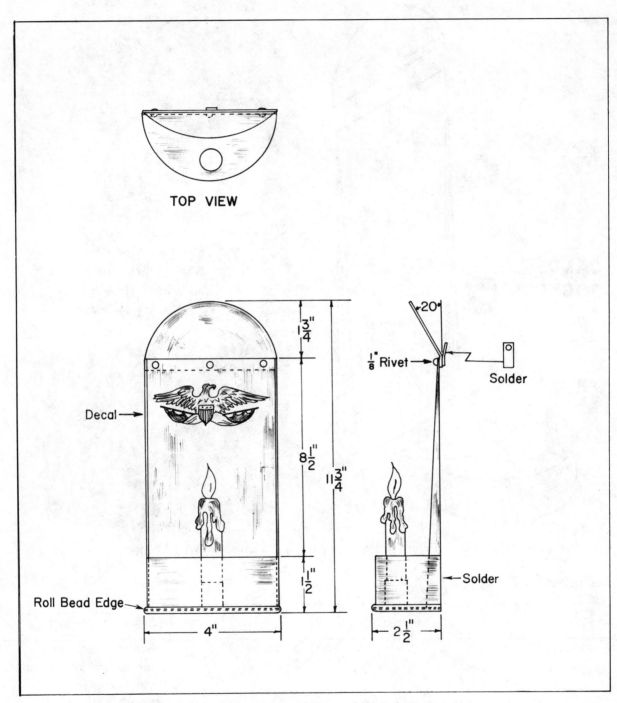

TOP VIEW

Decal →

$\frac{3}{4}$"

$8\frac{1}{2}$"

$11\frac{3}{4}$"

$1\frac{1}{2}$"

Roll Bead Edge →

4"

20°

$\frac{1}{8}$" Rivet

Solder

Solder

$2\frac{1}{2}$"

Fig. 2-10. Project Views of Wall Sconce

Construction Procedure

Cut the pieces according to dimensions in Fig. 2-10. Parts *C* and *D* are cut as a circle with a 4″ diameter and then cut in half. Lengthwise edges of part *A* are cut on a taper.

File all edges smooth.

PART A — BACK

Drill three ⅛″ evenly spaced rivet holes at the top edge.

Bend the tapered sides into right angles, using a bar fold.

PART B — CURVED FRONT

Bend and shape stock into a half circle, using a slip roll.

Roll bead the bottom edge to receive part *C*, using rotary machine.

Solder part *C* into bead edge of part *B* and solder the piece to part *A*.

PART C — BOTTOM

Solder a standard candle socket to the center as shown. (See Section I of Appendix for socket construction.)

PART D — TOP

Drill three ⅛″ rivet holes to match holes in part *A*.

Hammer the round edge into a scallop design. (Or crimper rolls on a rotary machine will make scallops.)

Bend the deflector out at a 20° angle.

Rivet part *D* to part *A*, using round head rivets.

Solder a wall hanger to the back of the sconce, as shown in Fig. 2-9.

Finish

The wall sconce may be decorated in different ways. It may be buffed with steel wool to look like pewter or painted flat black. An American eagle decal or other decals can be applied on either finish. See Section II of Appendix. If toleware effect is desired, hand-painted designs or decals are appropriate.

Tavern rules can be hand-printed on a piece of heavy parchment or other paper that is stained to look aged. The rules are glued to the sconce.

Tavern Rules

In Old English lettering, print:
1. Room and board — 5 pence per nite
2. Only two persons per room
3. Extra personage — 2½ pence more each
4. Bath (river water)—1½ pence
5. Bath (hot river water) — 3 pence
6. Stable and feed for ye mount— 1½ pence

or:

1. Ye shall not wear boots to bed
2. All fur-bearing animals killed in ye room belong to ye management
3. Ye shall not use yonder wash bowl for deposit of ye chewing wad
4. Tinkers must pay in advance

Strap Hinge Sconce

This sconce was a product of an ingenious old colonial farmer who had an extra strap hinge and, rather than waste it, converted it into a candleholder, Fig. 2-11.

Once the idea became popular, blacksmiths made and sold these sconces with a spear or rattail head design. If the entire length of the sconce was peened, it appeared to be a very artistic piece of work, Fig. 2-12.

Fig. 2-11. Strap Hinge Sconce

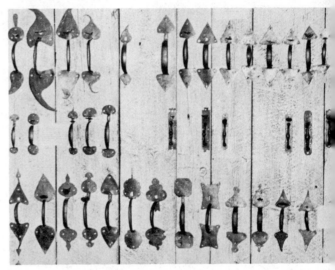

Fig. 2-12. Wrought Iron Steel Hinges and Handles (Sturbridge Village, Mass.)
Head designs can be adapted to shaping of other pieces.

Materials

Part	Pieces	Size	Suggested Material
A — Strap	1	3/16" × 1" × 22"	Hot rolled steel
B — Dish	1	2" dia. circle	26-gage sheet metal
C — Socket	1	¾" candle socket	26-gage sheet metal

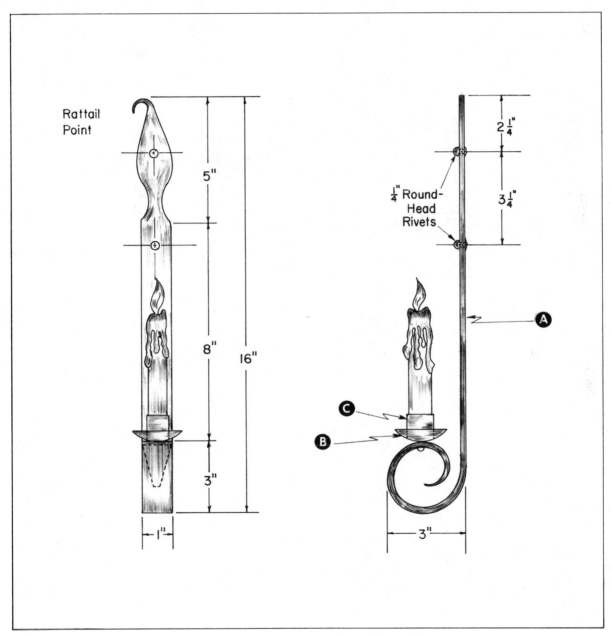

Fig. 2-13. Project Views of Strap Hinge Sconce

Construction Procedure

Lay out the design of your choice on flat band stock according to dimensions in Fig. 2-13.

Cut away excess material with hacksaw or chisel.

Heat the stock and shape the point. See Section I of Appendix for procedure.

Drill three evenly spaced ¼″ rivet holes in the strap. These holes receive ¼″ round head rivets for effect only. Drill a ⅛″ hang hole near the top of the point.

Heat and peen the entire surface. Remember to peen 5″ of the lower back side so that it will appear on the scroll work.

Reheat the piece and form the scroll. Drill a ⅛″ hole in the high point of the scroll to rivet the dish to the strap.

See Section I of Appendix for dish and socket construction.

Finish

The peening is the finish on the strap. With a wire brush go over the entire surface and brush or spray with clear lacquer. Drip dish and candle socket are painted flat black. Or, the entire project may be painted a flat black.

Masacksick Sconce

An abundance of candle sconces was necessary in colonial homes. Single candleholders sufficed for general lighting; but for concentrated lighting, multisconces were used. These fixtures, sometimes called *gang* sconces, took many forms; but perhaps the most popular was the three-arm or *trinity* multisconce, Fig. 2-14.

The sconce in Fig. 2-15 incorporates several designs. Its main feature is the *involute* shape or *spiral of Archimedes* which resembles a watch spring.

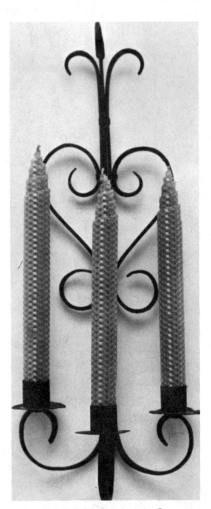

Fig. 2-14. Three-Arm Candle Sconce from the Federal Period (Henry Francis du-Pont Winterthur Museum)

Fig 2-15. Masacksick Sconce

Materials

Part	Pieces	Size	Suggested Material
A — Main stems	3	3/8'' × 25''	1/8'' flat band stock
B — Outside scrolls	2	3/8 × 12''	1/8'' flat band stock
C — Drip dish	3	2'' dia.	26-gage sheet metal
Candle sockets	3	¾'' dia.	26-gage sheet metal

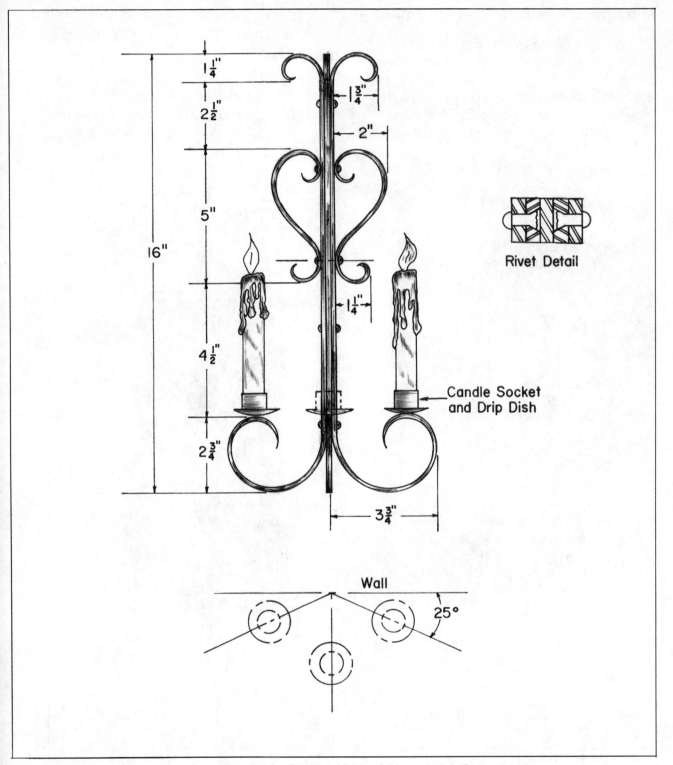

Fig. 2-16. Project View of Masacksick Sconce

Construction Procedure

Make a paper development (pattern) of the main pieces, making sure that the shape of the three stems closely match the stem detail in Fig. 2-16.

Cut the stock out and file the ends smooth.

PART A — MAIN STEMS

Heat and draw the ends of each of the three pieces to a point.

Reheat and form a small scroll at the top and a large scroll at the bottom of each piece.

Check each piece with the paper pattern and adjust, if needed.

Twist the center stem one-half turn just below and above the top and bottom scrolls. This permits the three pieces to present flat surfaces to each other for riveting.

Drill $1/8''$ holes in all three stems to receive rivets as they are shown in Fig. 2-16, and drill a $1/8''$ rivet hole in the high point of each large scroll to which drip dish and candleholder will be attached.

PART B — OUTSIDE SCROLLS

Heat and draw each end to a point.

Reheat and form a S-scroll to match your pattern.

Line up and mark two rivet holes to match those on the main stems, part A.

Drill two $1/8''$ rivet holes where marked.

NOTE: The two outside S-scrolls are riveted to the outside main stems before all three stems are fastened together. Countersink the holes on the under side of the main stems and peen the rivets so that a tight fit is possible when three stems are fastened together.

Rivet three main stems together.

PART C — DRIP DISH

Cut out three 2″-diameter drip dishes, shape them, and rivet them to the large scrolls on the main stems.

Rivet to scrolls.

Solder a standard candle socket to the center of each dish.

Finish

A flat black finish or a wire-brush finish may be applied. Designs, decorations, or decals are unnecessary, the scroll work being design enough.

Ship's Sconce

When old sea captains retired, they took several items from their ships. One of these was the ship's sternboard eagle, Fig. 1-4, which was placed over the doorway of the captain's home as an invitation to seafaring men to stop for a meal and a friendly talk.

Another item they took often was the ship's sconce. The spike sconce, Fig. 2-17, was driven into timbers, fastening it securely to the ship. The hang sconce, Figs. 2-18 and 2-19, had a double-candle, anchorlike pendulum. The weight of the arm and candles kept the sconce fairly level regardless of the ship's motion. The many variations of ship sconces — some plain, some fancy — all suggest the adventure of the open seas.

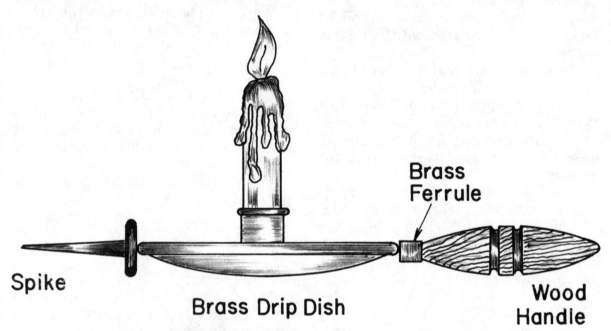

Brass Ferrule

Spike

Brass Drip Dish

Wood Handle

Fig. 2-17. Ship's Spike Sconce (From a Sketch by Cyril L. Marshall, Plymouth Plantation)
This sconce was the type used on an 18th-century ship, Biddeford, England.

Materials

Part	Pieces	Size	Suggested Material
A— Bracket	1	1″ × 11″	3/16″ flat band stock
B — Bracket arm	1	¼″ dia. × 8″	¼″ round stock
C — Anchor arm	1	¼″ × 14″	¼″ round stock
D — Crossarms	2	¼″ × 7″	¼″ round stock
Drip dish	2	2″ dia.	26-gage sheet metal
Candle socket	2	¾″ dia.	26-gage sheet metal

Fig. 2-18. Antique Hang Sconce
The loop on top allows sconce to
be hung from wall or ceiling.

Fig. 2-19. Ship's Sconce

Construction Procedure

Assemble and cut stock to size of
parts *A, B, C,* and *D.* See Fig. 2-20.

Lay out your choice of point design
for the hang, then cut away excess material from the stock with a hacksaw
or chisel.

File all edges and cuts smooth.

PART A — BRACKET

Heat and shape the points.

Reheat and peen the entire surface.

Drill three ¼″ holes; the first and
third should be in the center of the
points, and the second hole should be 1″
above the center of the stock. The first
and third holes will receive ¼″ round
head rivets for effect only, while the
second hole will receive part *B.*

PART B — BRACKET ARM

Heat and form the tip of this arm as
designed in Fig. 2-20.

Fit and weld part *B* into the second
hole in part *A.*

PART C — ANCHOR ARM

Heat and form an "eye" at the top
and a small scroll at the bottom. The
completed piece should measure 12″
overall.

PART D — CROSSARMS

Heat and form the crossarm scrolls
according to prescribed design.

Drill two ⅛″ rivet holes in the high
points of each scroll.

Solder candle sockets to drip dishes
and rivet piece to crossarms.

Weld crossarms to part *C.*

Finish

A flat black paint best enhances the
simple design, although a wirebrush
finish is suitable, if desired. No border
design or decal is necessary.

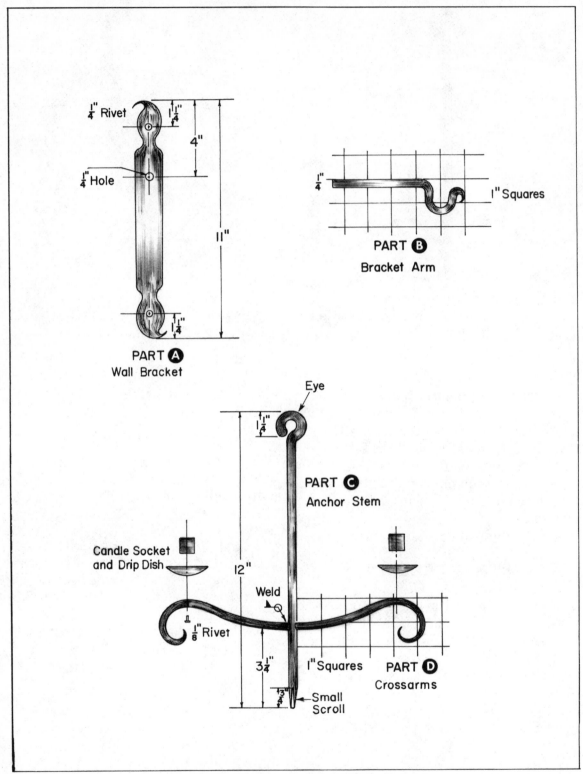

Fig. 2-20. Project Views of Ship's Sconce

Firelight

Fireplaces in colonial homes served for central heating, lighting, and cooking. They were so large that it has been said the colonists built their houses around them, and they took great care in their construction and in making fireplace equipment and cooking utensils.

The gang fireplace common in England soon appeared in the colonies. It was a unit of three or four fireplaces set back-to-back with a huge central flue or chimney. In this way a fireplace could be found in the living room, kitchen, and bedrooms. In such colonies as Virginia and Georgia where the climate was warm year-round and central heating was no problem, the main fireplace was placed outside the house to reduce fire hazard and keep the interior of the house cool.

Much of the equipment that colonial wives used in cooking hung in or on the fireplace, Fig. 3-1. Firetools, andirons, crane, and trivets, such as the reproductions included in this unit, were vital necessities to the colonists. Any of them would lend early American charm to the modern-day fireplace.

Fig. 3-1. Colonial Firetools and Equipment

(Shelburne Museum, Inc., E. J. Mengis)

Firetools

In all likelihood, the first poker was a straight stick. Because the stick would burn, settlers got the idea of using an iron rod instead. A blacksmith eventusally thought of putting a hook or spur on the end of the rod so that it was easier to turn logs and rake coals.

Soon blacksmiths made not only pokers, but flat shovels, forks, and brushes, turning out these firetools in unmatched sets. The shape of the handles depended upon the whim of the smith.

During the Federal Period of the late 1700's, matched sets with lathe-turned brass handles became popular, Fig. 3-2. The more common handles were in a heart shape, flat loop and ring, or eye, Fig. 3-3.

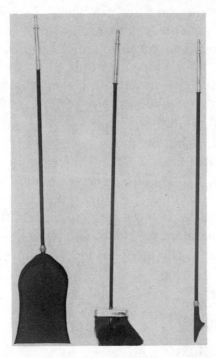

Fig. 3-2.   Handle Set from the Federal Period

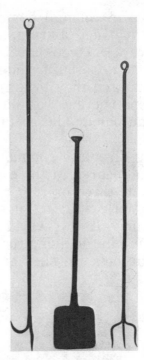

Fig. 3-3.   Firetools (Author's Collection)
              Not the different handle designs.

Materials

Part	Pieces	Size	Suggested Material
Shovel	1	4" × 6"	24-gage sheet metal
Brush	1	1½" dia.	Painter's dust brush
Main shaft	3	3/8" dia. (length to be determined)	Steel rod
Handles	3	¾" × 5"	Brass round stock for Federal design
(choose one type	3	3/8 × 20" × Pi	Steel rod for eye and ring
add to shaft lengths)	3	3/8" × 22"	Steel rod for heart shape
	3	3/8" × 30"	Steel rod for trinity shape

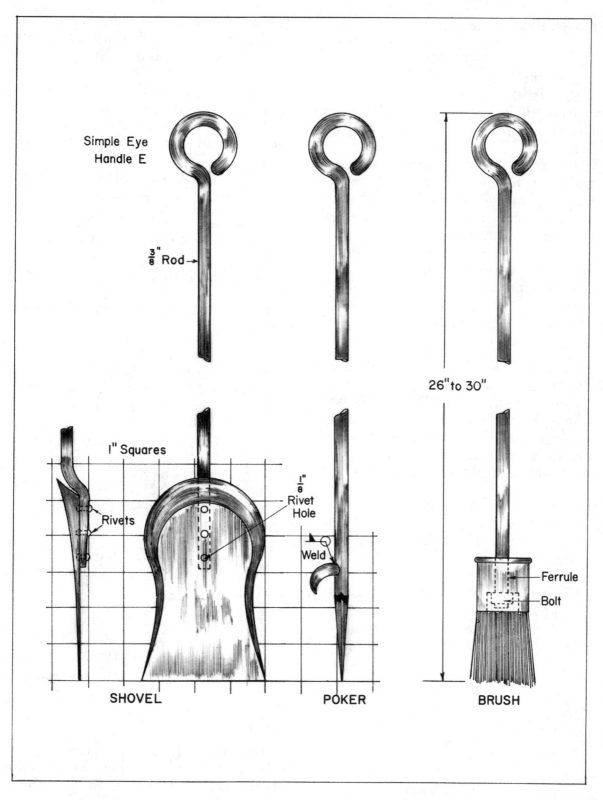

Simple Eye
Handle E

$\frac{3}{8}$" Rod →

26" to 30"

1" Squares

$\frac{1}{8}$"
Rivet
Hole

Rivets

Weld

Ferrule

Bolt

SHOVEL   POKER   BRUSH

Fig. 3-4.   Project Views of Firetool Set with Eye Handles

Construction Procedure

SHOVEL

Cut the shovel blank from 24-gage sheet metal.

Drill three evenly spaced, 1/8" rivet holes down the center, as shown in Fig. 3-4.

Insert the shovel blank between a male and female mold. (Molds may be made from 3/4" scrap plywood.) Use a vice, arbor press, or large C-clamp to press the molds together.

Remove the male mold member and finish the shovel shaping with a ball peen hammer. Remove blank from the mold.

File all edges smooth.

SHAFT

Heat and form the lower rod end as shown in Fig 3-4. Your choice of handle designs shown in Fig 3-5 will determine the length of the rod.

Drill three 1/8" rivet holes in rod to match holes in shovel blank.

Rivet the steel rod to the shovel.

BRUSH

Obtain a painter's dust brush and cut the handle off at the ferrule.

Drill a 3/8" hole in the center of the brush.

Thread the bottom of a 3/8" steel rod. (3/8"-18 NC threads).

Insert the threaded rod through the brush and fasten with a nut and washer.

POKER

Sharpen the bottom tip of a 3/8" steel rod.

Form a spur from a small piece of 3/8" rod and sharpen the point.

Weld the spur to the shaft.

HANDLES

The handle is a part or extension of the main shaft of the rod (except the Federal handle). It is shaped according to the desired design in Fig. 3-5.

EYE

Determine the size of the eye.

Multiply the diameter of the eye by pi and add the result to the shaft length.

Use an anvil, bench stake, or DiArco® bender to form the shape.

FLAT LOOP AND RING

Heat the top of the shaft and beat it flat.

Turn this flattened end into a small loop.

Insert a ring of any desired diameter into the loop.

HEART

Split the central shaft 4".

Heat and form the split end into a heart shape, using a bench stake and anvil.

Weld the two ends where they meet.

TRINITY

Heat and bend upper 10" of rod into a triangular shape with the two base angles being 45°.

FEDERAL PERIOD

Make a full-size layout to insure uniform grip. (This handle is a simple cyma curve.)

Lathe-turn 3/4" brass stock.

Cut 3/8" - 18 NC threads in interior of handle and on the 3/8" rod.

Screw the handle onto the rod.

Finish

Polishing with a wire brush will produce as suitable a finish as brushing with a flat black paint. Keep all brass work bright.

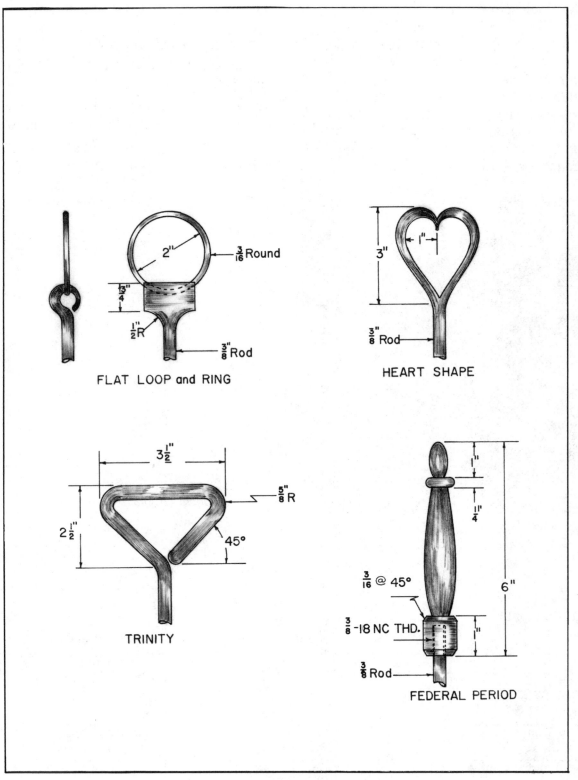

2''

$\frac{3}{16}$ Round

$\frac{3}{4}$''

$\frac{1}{2}$''R

$\frac{3}{8}$''Rod

FLAT LOOP and RING

1''

3''

$\frac{3}{8}$''Rod

HEART SHAPE

$3\frac{1}{2}$''

$\frac{5}{8}$''R

$2\frac{1}{2}$''

45°

TRINITY

1''

$\frac{1}{4}$''

6''

$\frac{3}{16}$ @ 45°

$\frac{3}{8}$-18 NC THD.

1''

$\frac{3}{8}$ Rod

FEDERAL PERIOD

Fig. 3-5. Alternate Handle Designs
(A) Flat loop and ring, (B) heart shape, (C) trinity, (D) Federal Period

Fireplace Crane

The crane, Fig. 3-6A, was developed not by accident or economy, but by necessity. It is a functional piece of equipment used to hold the large black pots over the fire during cooking, Fig. 3-6. The addition of this crane, Fig. 3-6A, to a modern-day fireplace helps recreate a colonial atmosphere.

Materials

Any size stock may be used, but it is essential that measurements are appropriate to size of the fireplace opening, Fig. 3-7. One-half inch round or square stock can be used for full-size cranes, while ⅜″ square or round stock is suitable for small openings.

Fig. 3-6A.   A Farmwife Cooks Thanksgiving Dinner at the Pliny Freeman Farm Fireplace (Old Sturbridge Village, Mass.)

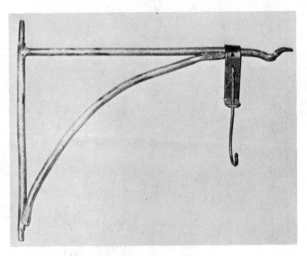

Fig. 3-6B.   Small Fireplace Crane and Trammel Hook

Part	Pieces	Size	Suggested Material
A — Arm	1	½″ × 20″-26″	½″ square or round stock
B — Main rod	1	½″ × 12″-16″	½″ square or round stock
C — Brace	1	3/8″ × 16″-20″	3/8″ square or round stock
D — Trammel	3	1″ × 7″	Flat band stock
	3	¼″ × 10″	¼″ round stock
Masonry hang for mortar joint	2		Heavy strap stock

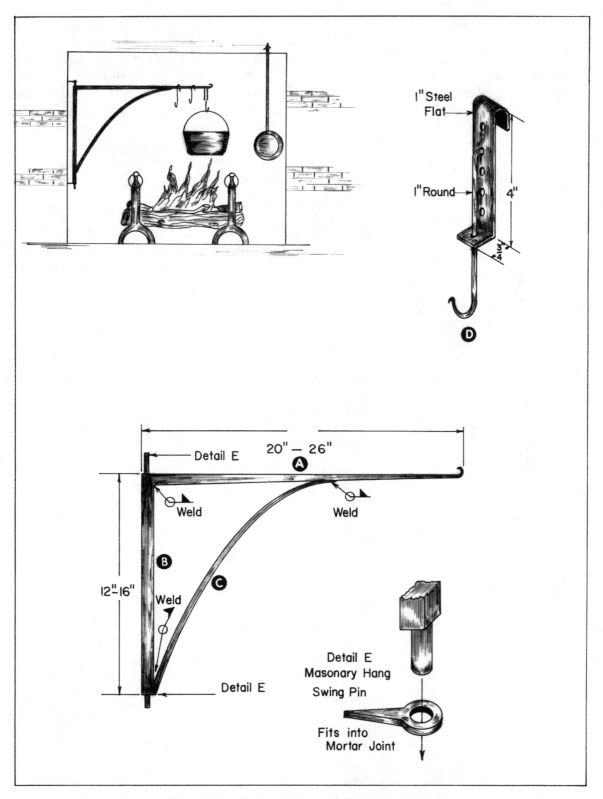

1" Steel Flat

1" Round

4"

3/4

D

20" — 26"

Detail E

A

Weld   Weld

B

12"–16"

C

Weld

Detail E

Detail E
Masonary Hang
Swing Pin

Fits into
Mortar Joint

Fig. 3-7.   Project Views of Fireplace Crane

Construction Procedure

PART A — ARM

Cut the stock to desired size.
Heat one end and draw-point it.
Reheat and shape this drawn point into a hook.

PART B — MAIN ROD

Cut the stock to size.
Heat both ends and drive them into the *pritchel* hole on an anvil to create pin shapes. (Note: the top pin should be longer than lower pin.)

PART C — BRACE

Cut the stock to desired size.
Heat and shape into an arc.
Reheat and shape ends to wrap around parts *A* and *B*.
Weld parts *A*, *B*, and *C* together as shown in Fig. 3-7.

PART D — TRAMMEL

Cut 1″ steel flat to size.
Drill several evenly spaced, ¼″ holes the entire length of piece.
Heat and shape the top of this piece into half round to fit over part *A*.
Bend bottom section to right angle.
Cut ¼″ steel round to size.
Heat and shape lower end into hook.
Heat and shape top end into right angle.
The hook is inserted through the ¼″ hole in the right angle of the steel flat, and the right angle on the other end of the hook is inserted into one of the holes in the steel flat.

Finish

A simple wire brush finish is most suitable for this piece of fireplace equipment.

Andirons

Andirons held the logs in the colonist's fireplace so that an underdraft allowed a fire to burn freely. Some andirons were equipped with a warming tray, Fig. 3-8, which could hold the food pots. Other andirons had a series of hooks, Fig 3-9, which permitted adjustment of the spits and cooking trays. Early andirons were heavy, plain and, most of all, functional. Later the colonists made andirons which were lighter weight and more decorative, often with brass lathe turnings.

The reproduction, containing a warming tray, has been reduced to size for modern-day fireplaces.

Fig. 3-8.   Andirons

Fig. 3-9.   Wrought Iron Andirons of the 17th Century (Metropolitan Museum of Art, Sylmaris Collection, Gift of George Coe Graves)

The loops held spits or large trays.

Materials

Part	Pieces	Size	Suggested Material
A — Uprights	2	2″ × 22″	½″ flat steel
Backirons	2	1″ × 23″	1″ square steel
Bar	1	¾″ × 24″	¾″ round steel
B — Tray brackets	2	½″ × 18″	3/16″ flat stock
C — Tray	1	5″ × 12″	1/8″ plate steel
Handle	1	½″ × 5″	1/8″ flat steel

NOTE: For fireplace openings under 30″ in height, reduce all dimensions by one-fourth.

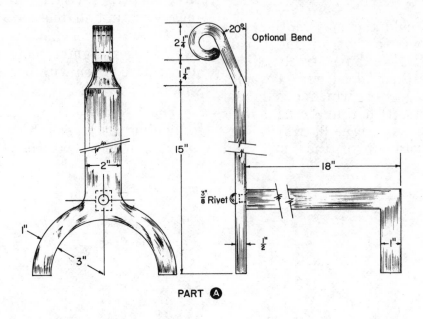

PART Ⓐ

Fig. 3-10. Project Views of Andirons

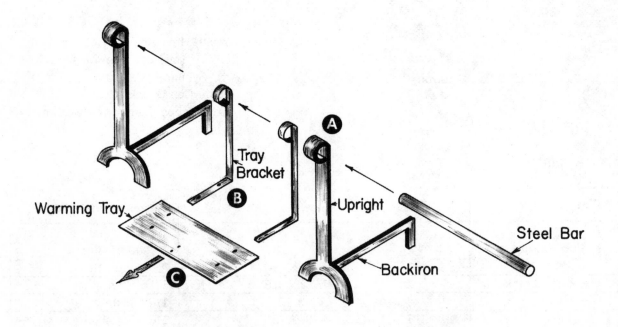

Fig. 3-11. Isometric Project Drawing of Andirons

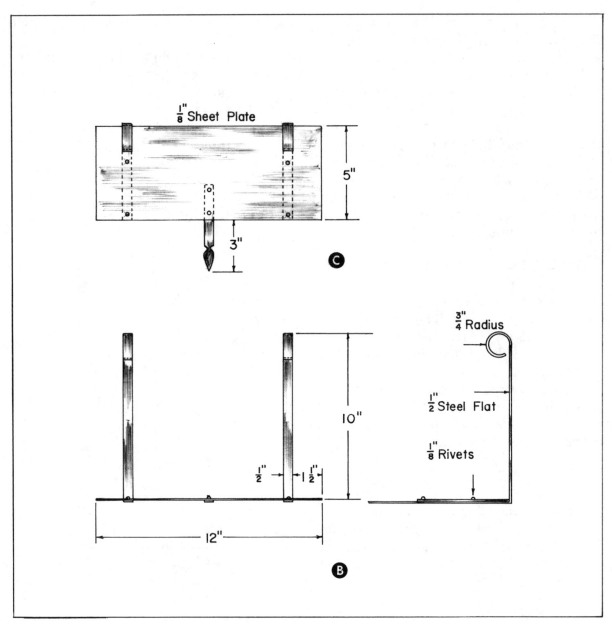

Fig. 3-12. Warming Tray Detail

Construction Procedure

NOTE: Plans are for andirons which include a warming tray. If a warming tray is not desired, the head of the andirons may be shaped to designs shown in Fig. 3-13. The same construction techniques are applicable.

PART A — UPRIGHTS, BACK IRONS, AND BAR

Cut and file $2'' \times 22''$ piece of flat steel stock.

Split the andiron uprights at dead center at the bottom ends.

Heat the pieces and pound them into a half-circle.

Heat the top cut and bend into a ring shape as shown in Fig. 3-11. The ring shape should be able to accommodate a ¾" steel bar.

Heat and form the ends of the back-irons into right angles.

Drill ⅜" countersunk hole just above the preformed half circle, and form a ⅜" rivetlike shank on the front of the back iron stock.

Insert this rivetlike shank through the predrilled hole and peen it over into the countersunk area.

PART B — TRAY BRACKETS
Cut and file two pieces of ½" × 18" flat stock for the tray brackets.

Drill two ⅛" rivet holes within a 3" area on the lower end of each piece.

Heat and bend the lower 3" into right angles.

Form the upper 2" of each piece into a ring having a ¾" radius.

Bend the spine of the piece to allow a free swing, Fig. 3-9.

PART C — TRAY
Cut and file a 5" × 12" piece of plate steel stock for the tray and a ½" × 5" piece of flat stock for the handle.

Heat and shape a point on the handle.

Drill two ⅛" rivet holes in tray and two in the end of the handle as shown in Fig. 3-12.

Rivet the handle to the tray and the brackets to the tray.

Insert a ¾" steel bar through parts A and C, Fig. 3-11.

Finish

All andirons are wire brushed. They are never painted.

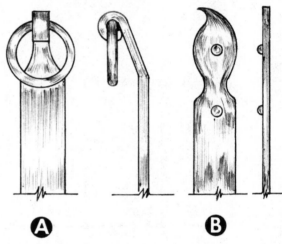

Fig. 3-13. Alternate Andiron Head Shapes without Warming Tray (A) Ring, (B) Rattail.

Cast Hessian Andirons

During the Revolutionary War, the British paid 30,000 mercenary German soldiers from the province of Hesse to fight in the English army. The Hessians, because of their professional and ruthless fighting, became the most hated among the enemy. After the war was over, Hessian andirons became popular, Fig. 3-15. Perhaps the idea started as a joke, or the colonists thought the best these mercenaries deserved was roasting. Figure 3-16 shows a reproduction suitable for the modern day fireplace.

Fig. 3-15. Andirons in the Shape of Hessian Soldiers (Henry Francis duPont Winterthur Museum)

Fig. 3-16. Reproduction of Hessian Andirons

Materials

Part	Pieces	Size	Suggested Material
A — Hessian soldier	2	17" long	Aluminum or brass
Gun	2	11 ¾" long	Aluminum or brass
B — Backirons	2	21" long	3/8", ½" round steel stock

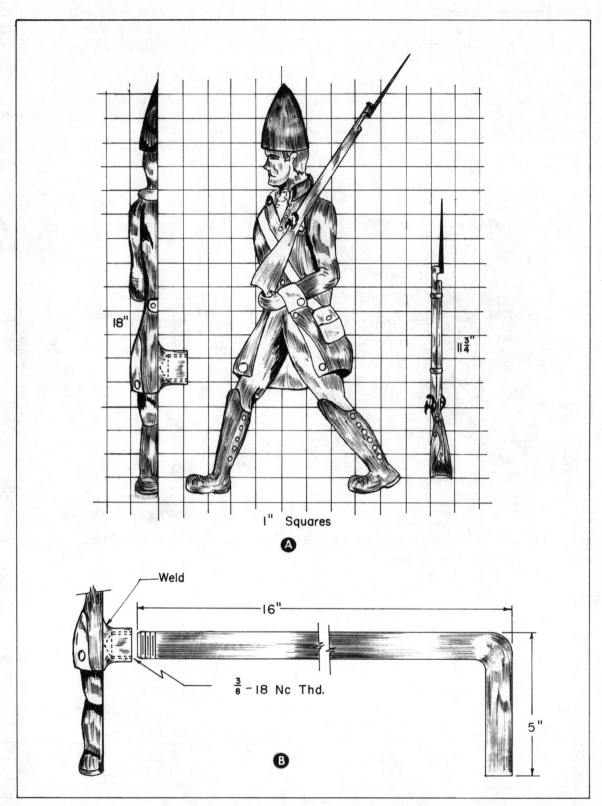

18"

11 3/4"

1" Squares

A

Weld

16"

3/8 - 18 Nc Thd.

5"

B

Fig. 3-17. Project Views of Hessian Andirons

Construction Procedure

PART A — HESSIAN SOLDIER AND GUN

Select a clear piece of white pine for the pattern mold. Draw a pattern for the soldier according to dimensions in Fig. 3-17. Make a separate pattern for the gun. Cut out on a band or jig saw.

Lay out details of the coat, boots, face, arms, hat, and gun on the patterns. Cut the details in with a sharp knife or wood carving chisels.

Sand the patterns smooth with all draft angles toward the front.

Cover the patterns with three or four coats of shellac.

Cast andirons, following the standard casting procedure with brass or aluminum. Place the sprue or pouring hole in the rear, just above the legs. This sprue is later threaded.

PART B — BACK IRON

Cut the round steel stock to size.

Heat and bend the rear of the back irons to a right angle. (Height must be obtained from the sprue hole in the Hessian upright irons.)

Reheat and shape the front of the back irons into a shank.

Cut male threads on the shank. (Any size will do.) Cut female threads into the remains of the sprue on the Hessian. The back irons screw into the upright irons.

Paint the Hessians and guns. Secure gun to Hessian with a rivet.

Finish

The soldier uprights are painted in bright colors. The long coat may be red, the trousers white or egg shell, boots brown or black, and the buttons gold. The pointed hat should be gold for officers or blue for enlisted men. A glaze of one-half flat black paint and one-half turpentine may be wiped over the finish, if an antique effect is desired.

NOTE:

These andirons are designed for use with a basket or wood dog which means they are removed when a fire is lit. Hessian irons are decorative. If the irons are to be used in fires, paint them with a fireproof flat black paint rather than colors.

Trivets

While trivets now serve mainly a decorative purpose, in the colonist's home they held hot pots of food, protecting wooden surfaces from burns. Blacksmiths made three-legged racks from wrought iron. Many different shapes existed, Fig. 3-18, the heart shape always being the favorite.

The trivet may be used in a modern home as a wall piece. A collection of all three shapes, Fig. 3-19, makes an interesting wall design.

Fig. 3-18. Colonial Trivets (Colonial Williamsburg)

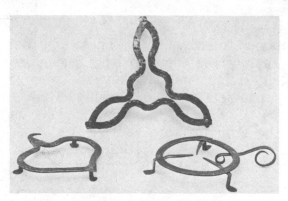

Fig. 3-19. Trivets, Heart Shape, Trinity, Ring

Materials

Part	Pieces	Size	Suggested Material
Heart shape	1	3/16" × 1" × 16"	Flat band stock
Legs	3	1/8" × ½" × 2 ½"	Flat band stock
Ring shape	1	3/16" × ½" × 19"	Flat band stock
Handle	1	3/16" × ½" × 7"	Flat band stock
Legs	3	3/16" × ½" × 4 ½"	Flat band stock
Trinity Shape	3	3/16" × ½" × 9"	Flat band stock
Legs	3	3/16" × ½" × 2 ½"	Flat band stock

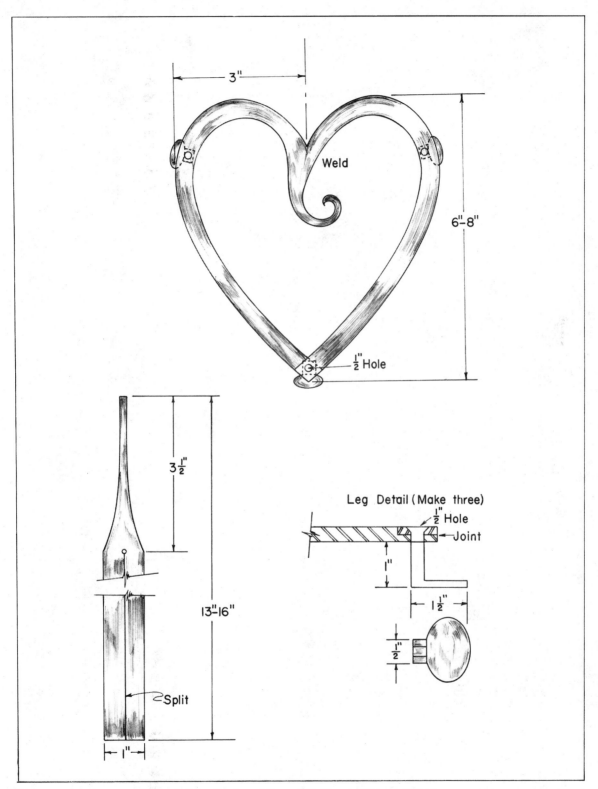

Fig. 3-20. Project Views of Heart Shape Trivet

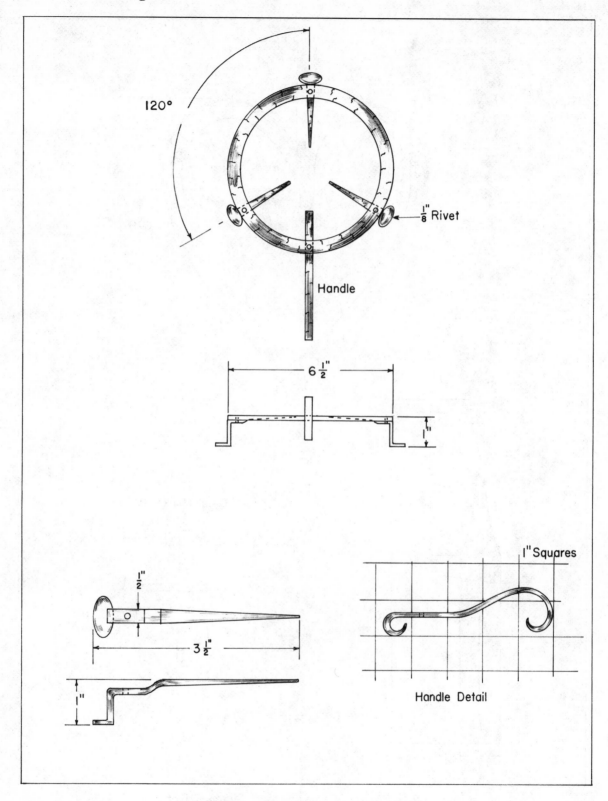

Fig. 3-21. Project Views of Ring Trivet

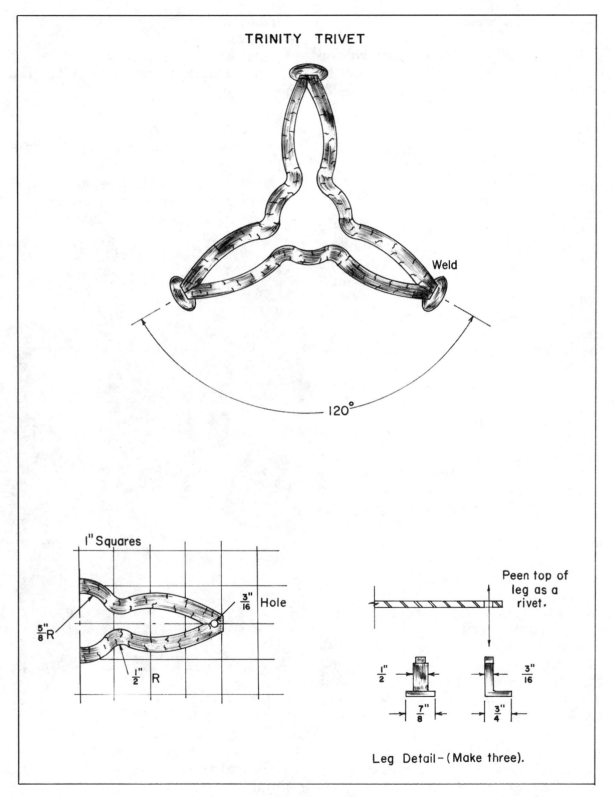

TRINITY TRIVET

Weld

120°

1" Squares

$\frac{3}{16}$" Hole

$\frac{5}{8}$"R

$\frac{1}{2}$" R

Peen top of leg as a rivet.

$\frac{1}{2}$"

$\frac{7}{8}$"

$\frac{3}{16}$"

$\frac{3}{4}$"

Leg Detail – (Make three).

Fig. 3-22. Project Views of Trinity Trivet

Construction Procedure

Make a full-size paper pattern for the design of your choice according to dimensions in Fig. 3-20, 3-21, or 3-22.

Cut the stock needed and file all edges smooth.

HEART SHAPE

Split the band stock lengthwise 12½″ and cut away excess material from the head shape.

Heat the stock and form the splits into a heart shape, using an anvil horn.

Reheat the stock and form a point inside the heart shape. The point should end in a small curl or hook.

Drill three ⅛″ countersunk holes in the stock. One at the bottom point of the heart, the other two in the curves, as shown.

LEGS

Cut the stock for the three legs.

Cut a ⅛″ × ¼″ rivetlike shank in the top of each leg.

Heat and shape the legs, as shown in Fig. 3-20.

Insert the leg shank into the countersunk holes in the heart and peen over as a rivet.

RING SHAPE

Heat the cut stock and form into a circle, using a DiAcro® bender, bench stake, or anvil horn.

Drill four ⅛″ rivet holes. Three holes (for the legs) are evenly spaced around the ring. The fourth hole (for the handle) is located halfway between two of the leg holes. See Fig. 3-21.

HANDLE

Cut the stock for the handle and file the ends smooth.

Heat and shape the handle into a scroll, as shown.

Drill a ⅛″ rivet hole where directed.

Rivet handle to ring with a ⅛″ flat head rivet.

LEGS

Cut the stock for three legs and file edges smooth.

Heat and shape the legs, as detailed.

Drill a ⅛″ rivet hole in each leg.

Rivet the legs to the ring.

TRINITY SHAPE

Make a full-scale paper development so that the three pieces of stock will match.

Cut the stock to size and file edges smooth.

Heat and shape the three pieces to conform to the pattern, Fig. 3-22.

Grind a V-groove in the butt joints of all three pieces.

Weld the three pieces together in a V-groove.

Drill three ⅛″ holes in the ends to receive the legs.

LEGS

Cut the stock for the three legs and file edges smooth.

Cut a ⅛″ × ¼″ rivetlike shank in the top of the legs.

Heat and shape the legs, as shown.

Insert the leg shank into the holes in the trinity and peen over as a rivet.

Finish

The trivets may be peened all over if desired. All trivets are wire brushed, a natural finish being more authentic. Paint is never applied.

Muzzlelight

Early settlers brought their guns with them. This gun was the *blunderbuss* — a short firearm having a funnel-type muzzle and capable of holding several shotballs. It was intended for shooting at close range without exact aim.

To meet their needs in the new land, colonists made rifles and pistols that were fit for long-range shooting. The rifle or shoulder weapon was a flintlock muzzle loader which fired pellets and lead balls. The pistol or *sidearm flintlock* was fired by spontaneous ignition. A small amount of powder was put in the *prime pan* leading to the powder charge inside the barrel and a *frizzen* (cover) put over the pan. When the *trigger* was pulled, the frizzen flipped open and a *hammer* holding a piece of flint fell down. When the flint struck the frizzen, sparks ignited the powder in the prime pan, setting off the charge in the barrel.

Naval cannons and fieldpieces were cast iron or brass. *Touchhole* firing and a smooth bore (interior barrel) were the main features of this weapon. A torch was touched to the *breech* of the chamber, firing the main charge. The charge was a large cannonball or *grapeshot* (chains, nails, and even bottles and rocks). These weapons were highly valued in the Revolutionary War. The fieldpieces captured at the Battle of Fort Ticonderoga were hauled across the New England wilderness in the dead of winter, Fig. 4-1, to be used by General Washington's army in the Siege of Boston.

Reproductions of the pistol, naval cannon, and fieldpiece make interesting paperweights, desk decorations, and lamp bases. Details are given in the working drawings.

Fig. 4-1. Lovell's Noble Train of Artillery (Dixon "Ticonderoga" Pencil Collection)

43

Pistol

The side arm or pistol, Figs. 4-2 and 4-3, was used mainly by gentlemen, sailors, and field officers. It was a single-shot weapon and required several minutes to reload. Gun manufacturers now offer reproductions of these pistols for gun collectors, gun clubs, and for contests in muzzle-load firing.

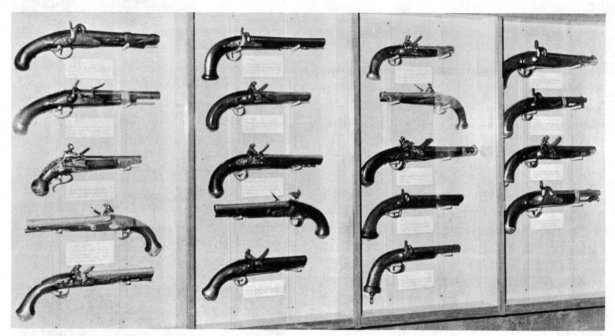

Fig. 4-2.   Pistol Collection   (Old Sturbridge Village)

Materials

Part	Pieces	Size	Suggested Material
A — Barrel	1	¾'' dia. × 11''	¾'' dia. steel or ¾'' casting
Sight	1	¼'' × ¾''	Scrap round or flat steel
Prime pan	1	3/8'' × ¾''	Scrap flat steel
B — Gunstock	1	¼'' × 4'' × 12''	White pine or similar wood
C — Hammer	1	1'' × 2'' × 3/16''	Flat steel
D — Trigger	1	1'' × 1'' × 3/16''	Flat steel
Trigger guard	1	½'' × 4 ½''	Flat steel or sheet metal
E — Side plates	2	1'' × 3''	Sheet brass or sheet metal
F — Butt plates	1	1 ¼'' dia.	Aluminum or brass round
G — Ram	1	1/8'' × 6''	1/8'' dia. steel or brass
	1	3/8'' × ¾''	3/8'' dia. steel or brass

Construction Procedure

NOTE:

The gun barrel, Fig. 4-4, may be made by one of three methods:
1. Casting and lathe turning,
2. Lathe turning on ¾″ diameter steel, or
3. Using a piece of ¾″ steel pipe with a plug in one end.

PART A — GUN BARREL

Cut the stock to required length.

Bore out a ⅜″ hole part way through the barrel to simulate the muzzle bore.

Lathe-turn the stock to suggested shape.

Steel wool to a satin sheen.

Drill one ⅛″ hole in the top of the barrel to receive the sight.

Drill a $\frac{3}{16}$″ hole in side of rear end of the barrel to receive the prime pan.

Drill and tap a ¼″ hole dead center bottom on the barrel. A ¼″ machine screw will fit here to hold the gun barrel to the wood gunstock.

SIGHT

Lathe-turn one end of a piece of steel scrap to a ball shape. Cut a rivetlike shank on the other end to fit into ⅛″ hole on barrel.

Force-fit the sight into the barrel.

PRIME PAN

Lay out the shape on a scrap piece of ⅜″ flat steel.

Cut out and file all edges smooth. Cut a $\frac{3}{16}$″ rivetlike shank on one side to fit in $\frac{3}{16}$″ hole on barrel.

Force-fit the prime pan into the barrel side.

PART B — WOOD GUN STOCK

Lay out the desired shape on white pine or similar wood.

Cut out the stock on a jig or band saw.

Chisel or cut a ¾″ trough using a router and core box bit, or a gouge chisel.

Place the barrel in the trough and mark the wood stock for the ¼″ machine screw.

Drill and countersink a ¼″ hole for the machine screw, and drill a ⅛″ in the stock to receive the ram.

Sand the wood gunstock smooth and round.

PART C — HAMMER

Lay out the hammer shape on a steel flat.

Cut out the hammer and file smooth.

Drill a $\frac{3}{16}$″ mounting hole in the center bottom of the hammer.

Fasten the hammer to the wood gunstock with a round head screw.

NOTE: The hammer must hit the prime pan when in a down position.

PART D — TRIGGER

Lay out the trigger shape on a piece of flat steel.

Cut the stock and file all edges smooth.

Insert the trigger into a slot cut in the wood stock and secure with a pin.

TRIGGER GUARD

Cut sheet brass or 26-gage sheet metal to size.

Hem both sides lengthwise $\frac{3}{16}$″.

Shape on a bench stake or anvil.

Drill one ⅛″ hole on each end of trigger guard.

Fasten to wood gunstock with two small screws.

PART E — SIDE PLATES

Lay out the shape and design on sheet brass or 26-gage sheet metal.

Cut the stock and file smooth.

Punch out design on side plates with engraving tools or prick punch.

Drill or punch a $\frac{1}{16}''$ hole on each end.

Fasten side plates to wood gunstock with small round head screws.

PART F — BUTT PLATE

Lathe-turn a piece of brass or aluminum round to shape.

Drill a $\frac{1}{8}''$ hole on dead center.

Fasten to wood stock with round head screw.

PART G — RAM

Lathe-turn a piece of scrap round into a $\frac{3}{8}'' \times \frac{3}{8}''$ slug.

Cut off a 6″ length of $\frac{1}{8}''$ diameter steel.

Force-fit the $\frac{1}{8}''$ diameter steel rod into the slug.

Insert the assembled ram into the predrilled hole of the wood gunstock.

Finish

All metal should be bright—the steel hammer, prime pan, trigger, trigger guard, barrel and plates. The wood gunstock is distressed, stained with a dark stain, and finished with shellac or lacquer. The finished pistol can be framed and mounted in a shadow box, Fig. 4-3.

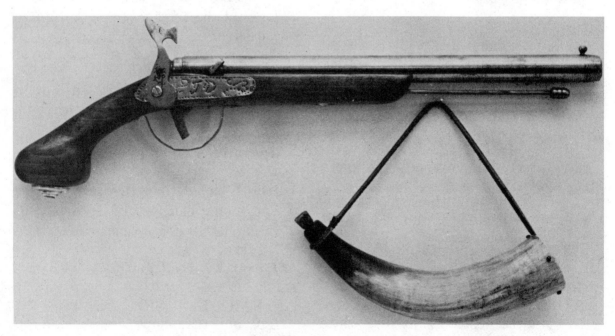

Fig. 4-3.   Percussion Cap Pistol

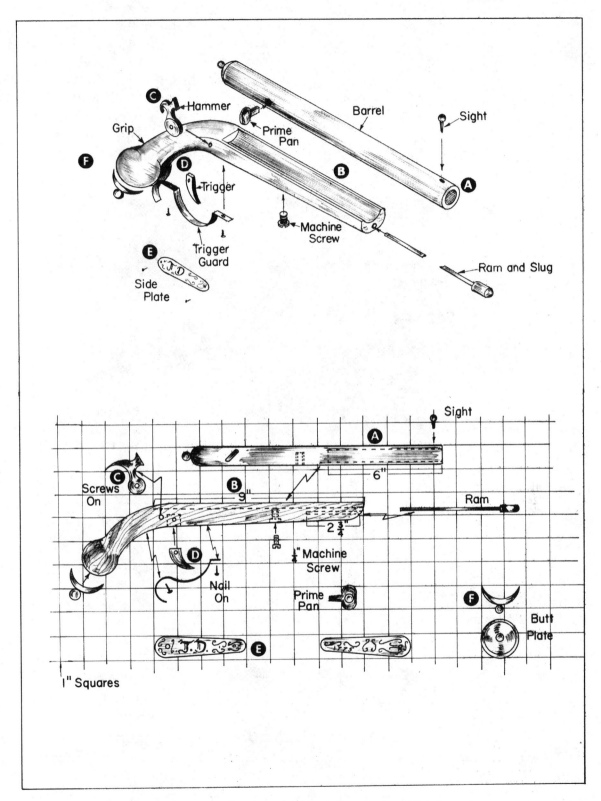

Fig. 4-4.   Project Views of Percussion Pistol

Naval Cannon

In August of 1812, the *USS Constitution* defeated Her Majesty's ship, the *Guerriere*, off the coast of Nova Scotia. "*Old Ironsides*," as the *Constitution* was called, had cannons that fired rounds of cannonballs from side ports, Fig. 4-5. The "sail-ripping rounds" were two or more balls connected together with a piece of chain. When fired, the balls spread apart and hit the enemy ship, tearing down sails and rigging. The reproduction of the "old 12-pounder" on the *Constitution* makes a good desk piece, Fig. 4-6, or two cannoons make suitable bookends.

Fig. 4-5.   12-Pound Naval Cannon on the Gun Deck of the United States Ship **Constitution** (Old Ironsides)

Materials

Part	Pieces	Size	Suggested Material
A — Barrel	1	¾" × 5 3/8"	¾" dia. brass, aluminum, or steel
Swing pin	1	¼" × 3"	¼" dia. metal
B — Carriage sides	2	2" × 4"	3/8" white pine
Carriage bottom	1	1" × 4"	3/8" white pine
Carriage end	1	1" × 1 ¼"	3/8" white pine
C — Axle timbers	2	3/8" × 3"	3/8" white pine
Axles	2	1/8" × 4"	1/8" dowels
Wheels	4	3/8" × 1" dia.	White pine
D — Ram	1	1/8" × 4"	1/8" dia. steel or brass
	1	3/8" × 3/8"	Scrap round steel or brass
Elevation wedge	1	½" × 2"	¾" white pine
Chain	1	#20	Brass chain
Powder keg	1	¾" × ¾"	Scrap pine
Swing pin straps	2	3/8" × 3"	Scrap sheet brass

Construction Procedure

PART A — BARREL

Lather-turn a piece of ¾″ diameter brass, steel, or aluminum, following the dimensions given in Fig. 4-7.

Drill a ⅜″ hole part way through the rod to simulate a muzzle bore.

Drill a ¼″ hole through the lower side of the barrel for the swing pin.

SWING PIN

Cut 3″ of ¼″ brass rod and insert it into the barrel. Solder in place.

PART B — GUN CARRIAGE

Lay out the two sides, the bottom timber, and the gun rest timber on ⅜″ white pine.

Cut out the stock and sand the ends smooth.

Score the sides of the carriage to resemble timbers. Use a V-groove chisel.

Distress entire wood stock lightly.

Assemble wood carriage using glue and small brads.

PART C — AXLE TIMBERS AND AXLES

Cut axle timbers from ⅜″ square white pine.

Drill a ⅛″ hole through each timber.

Cut axles from ⅛″ dowels and insert through timber holes.

Cut four wheels from a 1″ dowel or lathe turned white pine.

Drill a ⅛″ hole in the center of each wheel.

Fig. 4-6.   Naval Cannon

Insert wheels on axles and hold each in place with a small cotter pin.

Secure axle timbers to carriage using glue and small brads.

SWING PIN STRAPS

Lay out and cut small straps from scrap sheet brass.

Drill $\frac{1}{16}$" holes in several places along strap, as shown.

Shape a $\frac{1}{8}$" half-round in strap to fit over swing pin on barrel.

Place gun barrel on carriage and fit straps over pins. Fasten straps with very small brads or screws.

PART D — RAM

Lathe-turn a piece of scrap round to a slug $\frac{3}{8}$" × $\frac{3}{8}$".

Drill a $\frac{1}{8}$" blind hole lengthwise into slug.

Cut 4" of $\frac{1}{8}$" steel or brass round.

Force the $\frac{1}{8}$" round into the slug. Solder if needed. (Ram hangs on two hooks alongside the carriage.)

ELEVATION WEDGE

Lay out and cut a wedge from scrap pine, as shown.

NOTE: If desired, lathe-turn a small brass handle and insert it in the wedge. The wedge fits under the barrel breach and will raise or lower the cannon.

POWDER KEG

Lathe-turn a piece of white pine or dowel to resemble a keg.

Drill to insert a small link of chain for a handle. (The keg may be placed next to gun or hung from a hook on the carriage side.)

LOCK CHAIN

Fasten a length of #20 brass chain from one carriage side to the other, looping once over the elevation wedge. (The chain was used to hold the wedge in place while firing the weapon.)

To complete the authenticity of the cannon, pulleys, as shown, can be made to hang on the front and back of the piece. A rope can be tied as shown or hung on side of cannon.

Finish

Wood on the naval cannon should be distressed and stained a dark color. Apply three or four coats of lacquer and polish with paste wax. Brass work should be bright and protected from tarnishing.

NOTE:

Do not try to make these weapons fire. The suggested design and materials will not contain an explosive force.

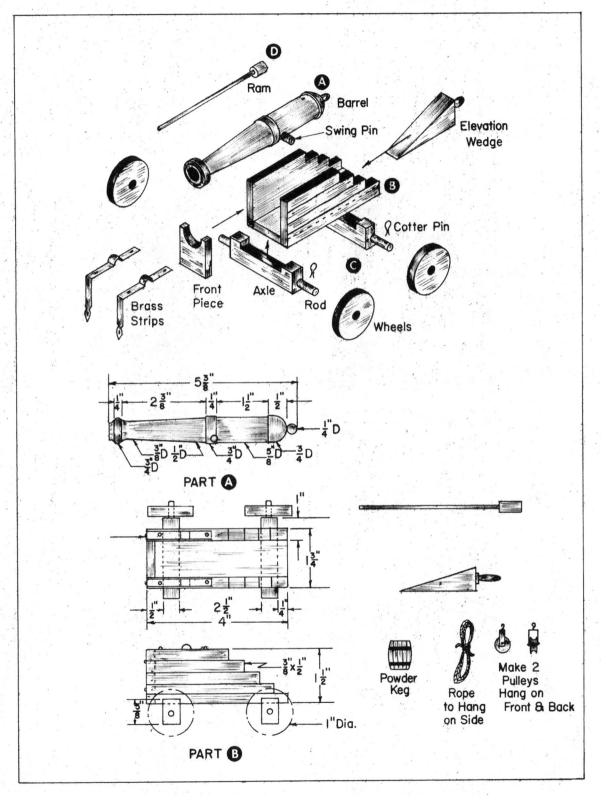

Fig. 4-7. Project Views of Naval Cannon

Fieldpiece

The only major difference between the naval cannon and the fieldpiece was that the fieldpiece had larger wheels for mobility on land. The carriage was made of heavy timbers. Teams of horses or oxen pulled these cannons from place to place.

A captured fieldpiece was considered a great prize. A fieldpiece used at the Battle of Yorktown to help win a decisive victory for General Washington is exhibited at Yorktown National Park, Fig. 4-8.

Reproduction of a field cannon suitable as a desk piece is shown in Fig. 4-9.

Fig. 4-8.   Revolutionary War Fieldpiece (Yorktown National Park, Va.)

Materials

Part	Pieces	Size	Suggested Material
A — Barrel	1	3/4" × 6"	3/4" dia brass, steel, or aluminum
Swing pin	1	1/4" × 2"	1/4" dia. brass
B — Carriage beams	2	3/8" × 6"	1/2" white pine
Crossbeam	1	1/2" × 3/4"	1/2" white pine
Tailbeam	1	3/8" × 1/2"	1/2" white pine
C — Axle timber	1	1/2" × 3"	1/2" white pine
Axle	1	1/8" × 4"	1/8" dia. maple dowel
Wheel rim	2	3/8" × 2 3/4" dia.	3/8" white pine
Wheel hub	2	3/8" × 3/8"	Maple doweling
Spokes	24	1/8" × 1"	1/8" dia. maple doweling
Tires	2	3/16" × 9"	Sheet brass strips
D — Ram	1	1/8" × 4"	1/8" dia. brass
	1	3/8" × 3/8"	
Swing pin straps	2	1/4" × 3"	Sheet brass strips
Powder keg	1	3/4" × 3/4"	White pine or dowel
Chain	1	#20 4" long	Brass chain
Elevation wedge	1	3/4" × 3"	1/2" white pine

Construction Procedure

PART A — BARREL

Cut 3/4″ diameter brass, steel, or aluminum to required length.

Lathe-turn to shape and size in Fig. 4-10.

Bore a 3/8″ blind hole lengthwise in barrel to simulate a muzzle bore.

Drill a 1/4″ hole through barrel for the swing pin.

NOTE: The swing pin should be forward from the balance point so the breech will remain down.

PART A — SWING PIN

Cut 1/4″ diameter brass to size. Insert into hole through barrel and solder in place.

PART B — CARRIAGE

Lay out all parts and shapes on white pine.

Cut out the stock on jig or band saw.

Distress the timbers to simulate hand-hewn beams.

Sand all timbers and beams smooth, and stain.

NOTE: The crossbeam and the tailbeam are fastened to the side timbers with glue and dowels.

PART C — AXLES AND WHEELS

Lay out and cut axle timbers.

Drill a 1/8″ hole through the axle timber.

Cut the 1/8″ maple dowel and insert into a hole in timber. Fasten with glue.

Fasten the axle timber to the carriage with glue and dowels.

WHEELS

NOTE:

Cast wheels may be used if desired. File the casting smooth and drill a mounting hole in the hub. Secure to the 1/8″ dowel axles.

WOOD WHEELS

Lathe-turn a 3/8″ piece of dowel for hub, according to shape shown in Fig. 4-10.

Fig. 4-9.   Fieldpiece

Drill a ⅛″ hole in the center of the hub for axle .

Lathe-turn white pine to rim shape and size, 2 ¾″ dia. ×⅜″ × ⅜″.

Divide wheel rim into 12 equal parts and mark for location of spokes.

Drill twelve ⅛″ holes through the rim.

Lay out paper drawing of the wheel, holding the hub and rims in place with pins. Wheels will be assembled on this pattern to insure accuracy.

Cut the ⅛″ maple dowels for the spokes and sand the ends.

Stain all wheel parts before assembly.

Glue the spokes to the rim and the hub.

NOTE: Force the ⅛″ spokes through the rim into the hub. The spokes may stick out from the rim. When dry, the spokes are cut flush with the rim and sanded smooth. Restain, if necessary.

WHEEL TIRES

Cut strips of sheet brass and file the edges smooth.

Fit the strips around the wheel rim tightly and solder tire together.

Mount the wheels to the axle timbers and secure with small cotter pins or wedges.

PART D — RAM

Cut 4″ of ⅛″ brass round.

Lathe-turn a slug of brass round into a ram shape.

Drill a ⅛″ blind hole in the brass slug.

Force ⅛″ brass round into the hole in the slug. Solder if necessary.

Secure the ram to the carriage by means of two brass hooks on the side of one timber.

SWING PIN STRAPS

Lay out and cut two swing pin straps from brass sheet stock.

File the edges smooth and drill several $\frac{1}{16}$″ mounting holes. See Fig 4-10.

Fit the straps over the timbers and shape a half round to fit over the swing pins in the cannon barrel.

Secure the straps to the carriage by means of brass brads or round head screws.

POWDER KEG

Lathe-turn a piece of ¾″ white pine or dowel into a keg shape.

Drill two $\frac{1}{16}$″ holes on the top edge and use a piece of brass chain for a handle.

Secure the keg to the carriage timbers or axle timber with a small brass hook.

NOTE: A single link of #20 chain when opened will make an excellent hook.

Cut two pieces of #20 brass chain and secure to carriage. One chain is used for hauling, the other to lock the elevation wedge in place.

ELEVATION WEDGE

Lay out and cut a small wedge, sand, and stain.

Lathe-turn a small brass handle if desired and insert into wedge.

Insert wedge under cannon breech at the tail beam.

Finish

Use a dark stain over the distressed wood parts. Finish with shellac or lacquer and paste wax. All brass work should be bright and protected against tarnishing.

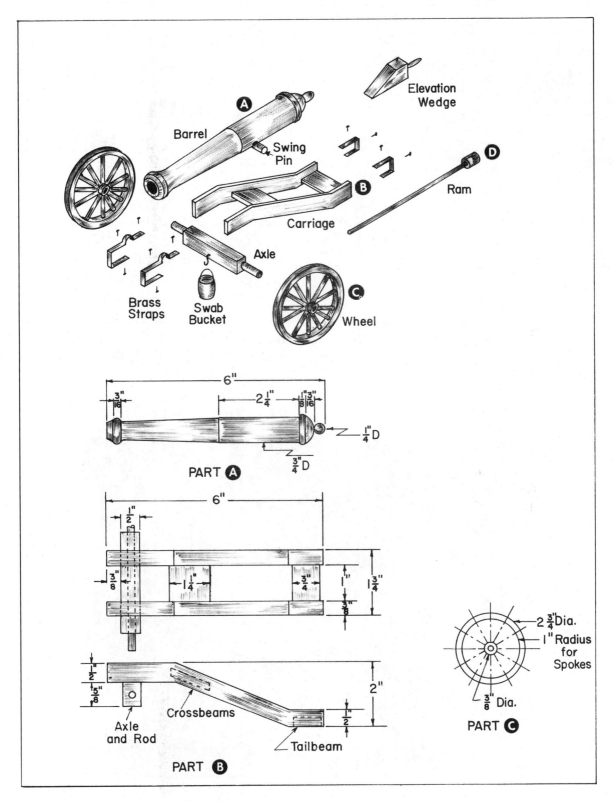

Fig. 4-10. Project Views of Fieldpiece

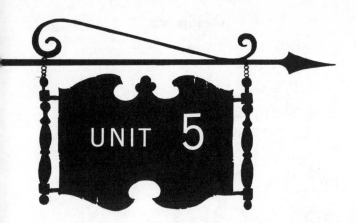

UNIT 5

Forgelight

Every little hamlet had its blacksmith; larger towns often had several, Fig. 5-1. Blacksmiths were responsible for everything from shoeing horses to making ornamental ironwork. Fine ornamental iron often took the form of candle sconces, chandeliers, door knockers, foot scrapers, firebacks, andirons, and signs. New Orleans "iron lace" used on wrought iron fences, gates, railings, and balconies is a lasting example of exterior ornamental iron.

The village smith was called upon to make outdoor signs to replace earlier wood pieces, iron lanterns for town lighting, iron chandeliers for taverns and private homes, and weather vanes.

Reproductions in this section are all exterior metalwork. The reproductions combine function with design and can be made from standard stock sizes or sheet metal. Refinements may be imposed upon these objects if desired.

Fig. 5-1. Blacksmith Hand-Forges Ironwork As Did His 18th Century Predecessors (Deane Forge and Shop, Colonial Williamsburg)

56

Name Sign

Signs were more significant in colonial days than now. Since no street numbers or street names existed, people gave their addresses as related to large or well-known landmarks. A colonist gave such directions as, "Four houses on the left, past the Three Crowns Inn."

Because many early colonists could not read, the signs, often copies of signs used in mother England, were made or designed into something easily recognizable.

Oversized horseshoes, books, shears, or models of boats served as signs for tradesmen. Sometimes the names of well-known people appeared on signboard of colonial inns, Fig. 5-2, while other taverns were identified by such unique names as "The Bag-O-Nails" or "The Silent Woman."

Materials

The sign in Fig. 5-3, is greatly reduced from the size of colonial signboards. The addition of the family name makes it functional for modern usage. The silhouette at the top of the sign could be a horse, boat, duck, or lamp-lighter. Minor adjustments will be necessary, depending upon the length of the last name.

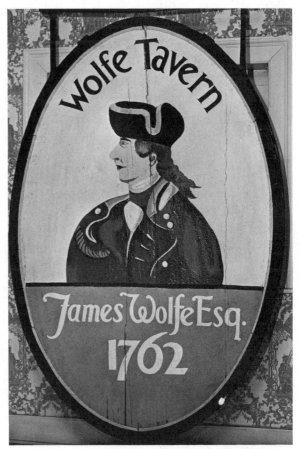

Fig. 5-2.   General Wolfe Signboard (Newburyport Historical Society, Mass.)

Part	Pieces	Size	Suggested Material
A — Mounting Bracket	1	3/16" × ½" × 37"	Flat band iron
B — Name Shield	1	8" × 14"	20-gage sheet metal
C — Silhouette	1	8" × 14" (Typical)	20-gage sheet metal

Construction Procedure

Lay out a paper drawing or development for the shield and the silhouette. (The silhouette may be cast if desired; see Fig. 5-10, 5-11, or 5-12.)

Transfer the drawings to the sheet stock and cut the outlines.

File all edges smooth and free of burrs.

Cut the band stock to size and file end smooth.

PART A — BRACKET MOUNT

Make two scroll bends in the bracket using a DiAcro® bender, bench stake, or anvil horn.

Lay out and drill two $\frac{1}{4}$″ countersunk mounting holes in the bracket as indicated.

Lay out and drill two $\frac{1}{4}$″ holes to receive the cotter pins for hanging the shield.

Lay out and drill four $\frac{1}{8}$″ holes between the cotter pin holes for riveting on the silhouette. Number of rivets is dependent upon size and weight of silhouette.

Make a right-angle bend in the bracket where directed.

PART B — NAME SHIELD

Lay out and drill a $\frac{3}{16}$″ hole in the two high points of the shield to take the S-hooks.

PART C — SILHOUETTE

Make a $\frac{3}{8}$″ right-angle bend in the bottom of the silhouette.

Lay out and drill four rivet holes in base to match those on bracket.

Rivet the silhouette to the bracket with $\frac{1}{8}$″ flat head rivets. Insert cotter pins into the bracket holes from the bottom and open them up. (The head of the cotter pin is toward the shield.) Insert an S-hook through the shield holes and the cotter pin heads.

Finish

Usually the shield is finished in flat black paint with Old English or other style of lettering in white.

Bright, natural colors on the silhouette enhance the finished project. The lamplighter, as an example, may have a green coat, brown trousers, red hat, black shoes and hair, and gold buttons. Ducks and other animals can be painted in natural colors.

Fig. 5-3.   Old Lamplighter Name Sign

Fig. 5-4.   Project View of Old Lamplighter Name Sign and Alternate Designs

Weather Vane

Vanes such as the one shown in Fig. 5-5, were common in New England for two reasons: (1) they were an interesting pastime for early colonists who loved to tinker and carve during long winters, and (2) they provided a good indication of what might be expected next from the changeable New England weather.

One of the oldest and most famous weather vanes was the Deacon Shem Drowne's copper grasshopper which was located for over 100 years on top of Fanueil Hall in Boston. Today, many colonial homes have a metal weather vane fastened to a cupola, a steeple like structure on the roof peak, Fig. 5-6.

Fig. 5-5.   Colonial Eagle Weather Vane (Shelburne Museum, Inc., E. J. Mengis)

Materials

Part	Pieces	Size	Suggested Material
A — Main stem	1	28''	3/8'' dia. steel
Roof mount	1	12''	1'' flat steel
B — Direction arms	4	3/8'' × 8''	1/8'' flat steel
Arm holder	1	4''	¾'' dia. steel
Letters	4	4'' × 4''	20-gage sheet metal
C — Arrow arm	1	½'' × 20''	3/16'' flat steel
Arrow holder	1	3''	¾'' dia. steel
Silhouette	1	10'' × 12'' (Approx.)	20-gage sheet metal

Construction Procedure

NOTE:

Weather vane may be constructed with or without a silhouette. Figs. 5-6, 5-7, 5-8, 5-9, 5-10, 5-11, and 5-12 suggest silhouettes, any of which may be cast if desired. See Casting, page 74.

Cut 3/8" diameter steel to length.

Lathe turn or grind a ball-like tip on one end. (This tip fits inside the arrow-arm holder.)

Cut the stock for the roof mount.

Drill a 3/8" hole in the center of the roof mount to receive main stem, and countersink 3/8" hole on each end for fastening to roof.

Weld the main stem into the center 3/8" hole on the roof mount.

PART B — DIRECTION ARMS

Cut to size the flat band stock for arms and 3/4" diameter steel for holder.

Lathe turn the holder to shape shown.

Drill a 3/8" hole lengthwise through the holder.

Cut an "X" slot in the top of the arm holder to take the four directional arms. The fit should be snug.

Drill a 1/8" hole in one end of each direction arm to receive the directional letters.

Weld the directional arms to the holder.

Cut the letters for the four directions from sheet metal and file all edges smooth.

Punch or drill a 1/8" hole in all of the letters.

Rivet the letters to the ends of the directional arms.

PART C — ARROW

Cut the band stock for the arrow.

Drill 1/8" holes on each end of arrow to accommodate arrowhead and feather, Fig. 5-7.

Cut the stock for the arrowhead, feather, and silhouette from sheet metal.

Drill or punch 1/8" holes in the arrowhead and feather to match the holes made in the ends of arrow.

Rivet the head and feather to the arrow.

Drill or punch several 1/8" holes in the bottom of the vane silhouette.

Drill matching holes in the arrow.

Rivet the silhouette to the arrow.

ARROW HOLDER

Cut 3/4" steel round to size suggested.

Lathe turn steel round to shape.

Drill a 3/8" hole part way through steel round. The main stem will fit in this hole.

Cut a slot in the top of the arrow holder to take the arrow arm.

Weld the arrow arm with its silhouette to the holder.

NOTE: Fill the 3/8" hole in the arrow holder with grease before installing vane on roof. Roof brackets may need adjustment to fit your roof pitch.

Finish

Use a flat black finish paint on the ironwork. The silhouettes and letters can be coated with gold, bronze, or copper, or painted in natural colors.

(A) Figure is made of sheet metal
(Farm Museum of Landis Valley, Penn.)

(B) Horse measures 28″ long × 16½″ high.
Fig. 5-6. An Iron Horse Often Decorated Weather Vanes

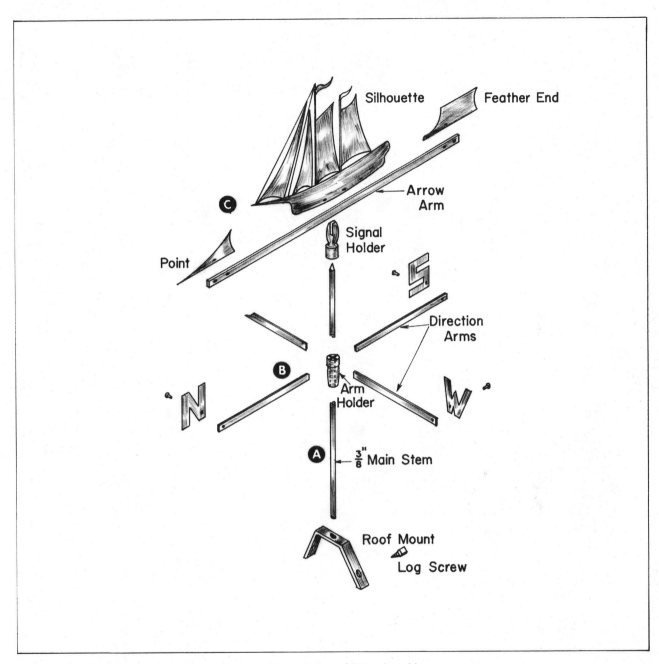

Fig. 5-7. Project Views of Weather Vane

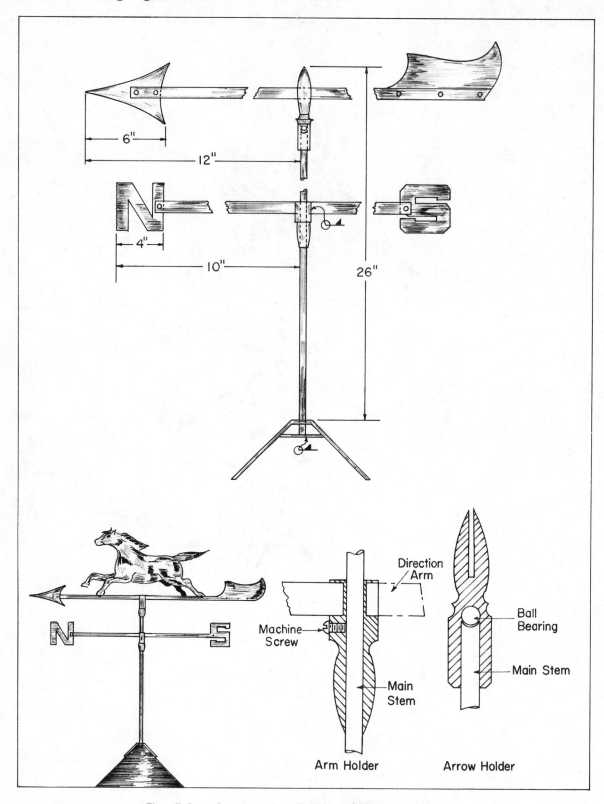

Fig. 5-8.   Construction Details of Weather Vane

Fig. 5-9. Project View of Eagle and Directional Letters

I" Squares

Fig. 5-10. Project View of Colonial Minute Men

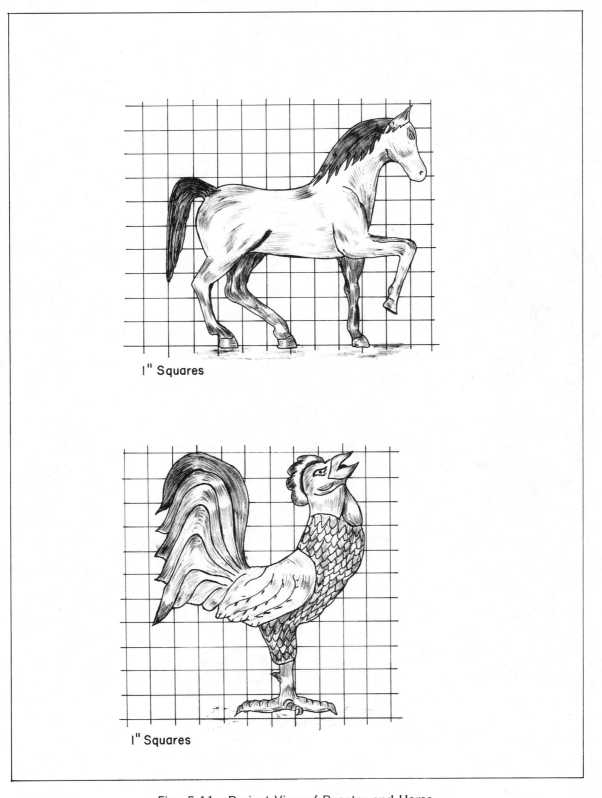

1" Squares

1" Squares

Fig. 5-11. Project View of Rooster and Horse

Fig. 5-12. Castmasters
Wood and plastic units were used to form a mold.

Outdoor Light

Before public street lighting became a practice in many towns, individuals carried *waylighters* (lanterns). As towns began to provide street lamps, coppersmiths and tinsmiths turned out sheet metal polelamps. Blacksmiths, in turn, made wrought iron lamps illuminated by candles.

The town lamplighters would make the rounds at dusk lighting the lamps hanging from high poles, and at dawn would return to extinguish them. These lamps were used inside dwellings as well as outside, Figs. 5-13, 5-14, and 5-15. Two of the most well known styles were the Williamsburg and the Bunker Hill lanterns, Fig. 5-16.

Materials

The lamp shown in Fig. 5-17 can be made of sheet metal, sheet brass, or tinplate, bronze or copper sheets.

Fig. 5-13. Lamps Used in a Boot Shop

Part	Pieces	Size	Suggested Material
A — Bottom pan	1	8'' × 9''	24-gage sheet stock
B — Side rails	4	1 ½'' × 9''	24-gage sheet stock
Top rails	2	1 ½'' × 8''	24-gage sheet stock
	2	1 ½'' × 9''	24-gage sheet stock
C — Top cover	1	11'' × 12''	24-gage sheet stock
Sides of top cover	1	10'' dia.	24-gage sheet stock
D — Glass clips			
Lower	4	1'' × 6'' (Approx.)	Scrap 24-gage stock
Upper	4	1 ½'' × 6'' (Approx.)	Scrap 24-gage stock
E — Glass protectors	8	1/16'' × 12'' (Approx.)	Coat hangers or round stock
Glass	4	8'' × 9''	Single strength window glass

Fig. 5-14. Lamp of Sheet Metal

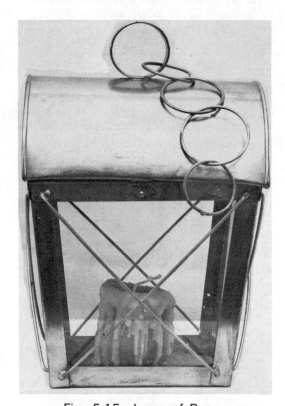

Fig. 5-15. Lamp of Brass

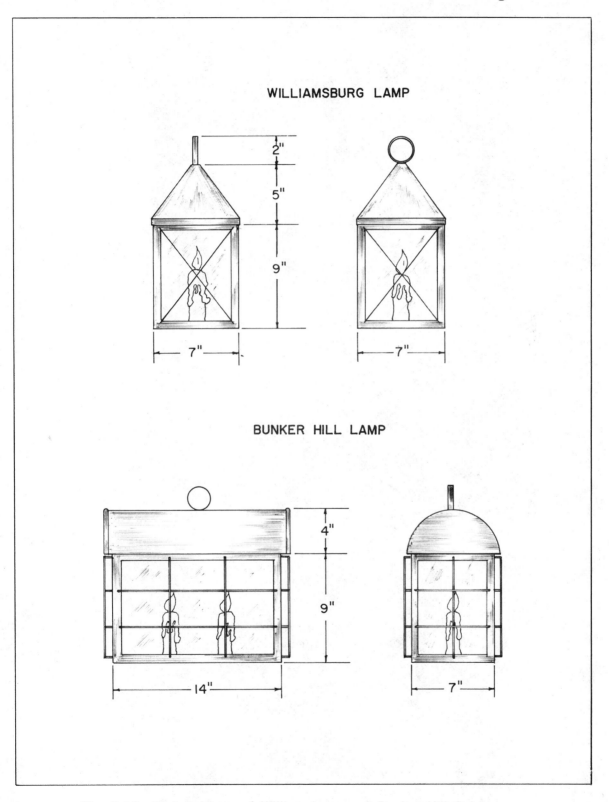

WILLIAMSBURG LAMP

BUNKER HILL LAMP

Fig. 5-16. Project Views of Williamsburg and Bunker Hill Polelamps

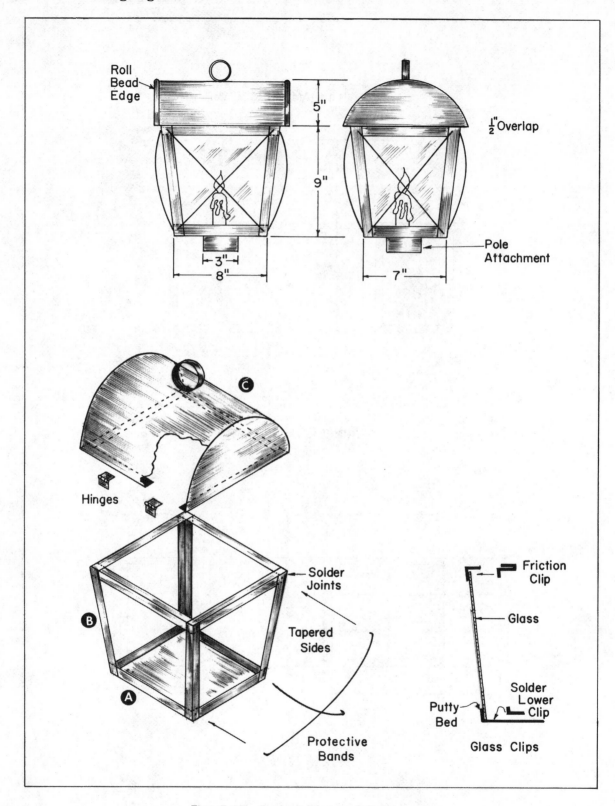

Roll Bead Edge

5"

9"

3"

8"

$\frac{1}{2}$" Overlap

7"

Pole Attachment

Hinges

Ⓒ

Solder Joints

Ⓑ

Tapered Sides

Ⓐ

Protective Bands

Friction Clip

Glass

Solder Lower Clip

Putty Bed

Glass Clips

Fig. 5-17. Project Views of Polelamps

Construction Procedure

Lay out and cut sheet-stock parts as shown in Fig. 5-17.
File all cuts and edges smooth.

PART A — BOTTOM PAN
Lay out and mark the bends required.
Bend the lips at a right angle on a bar fold or pan break.
Drill or punch a 1/8" hole in each corner (8 in all).

PART B — SIDE RAILS
Bend the side rails in half lengthwise.
Place Parts B against Part A and mark for 1/8" matching holes.
Drill or punch the holes.
Solder Parts B to Part A, keeping the holes free of solder.

TOP RAILS
Bend the top rails in half lengthwise.
Solder the top rails to the tops of Part B so that a box-like shape is made.
Drill or punch holes at each end to match the holes in the bottom.

NOTE: A hardboard template will help keep the work square while soldering. This same hardboard will be helpful when the glass clips are soldered.

PART C — TOP COVER
Roll the top cover in a slip roll to create a half round.
Roll bead the two curved edges to receive the ends.
Bend other edges at a right angle to receive the hinges and hasp, as shown.

TOP ENDS
Cut the 10" diameter circle in half.
Solder the two halves into the bead in the top cover.
Solder two 1" hinges and a hasp to the cover and the top rails.

PART D — GLASS CLIPS
Make glass clips according to shapes shown in Fig. 5-17.
Solder the lower clips to bottom pan, using the hardboard template as a spacer.

PART E — GLASS PROTECTORS
Make the wire protectors, shaping them as shown.
Solder the protectors in the holes of side rails.

GLASS
Putty the inside edges of the bottom pan, side and top rails.
Cut the glass, using the hardboard template as a guide.
Install the glass against the putty and install the top glass clips.
Solder a ring on the cover if desired.

Finish

If sheet brass or copper is used, polish it and protect it against tarnishing. If sheet metal is used, coat it with a pewter tone, flat black paint or spray finish of your own choice. (See Section II of Appendix for finishing instructions.)

Casting

After the colonies became settled, ironworks began to spring up in a very crude type of strip mining. The iron was not of good quality, but it was cast, nevertheless, as firebacks, oven doors, and andirons.

The remainder of this section deals with cast reproductions. Figs. 5-9, 5-10, and 5-11 are cast silhouettes which have been suggested for use on name signs or weather vanes.

Construction Procedure

Lay out a paper development for the proposed silhouette.

Transfer the paper drawing to a clear piece of pine.

Cut out the shape with a jig or band saw.

Create draft angles by sanding or chiseling the mold master.

Sand the mold master smooth.

Paint the master with two or three coats of paint or lacquer. (A coat of paste wax will help in later removing the mold from the casting sand.)

In casting, follow standard foundry procedures. *Patternmaking and Founding* by R. E. Smith is one of the books which gives instruction for this operation.

An Example of Cast Reproduction

Cast Bell

Colonists had to rely on public notices or word-of-mouth for the news of the day. Sometimes the lamplighter was also the *town crier* who walked through the streets shouting, "Hear Ye, Hear Ye," and ringing a hand bell to gain attention. Once a small crowd gathered, he would read the news of the day. The small brass bell was his stock-in-trade.

Larger bells, mounted on rooftops, spread the alarm for a fire, called town meetings, or tolled the death of a townsman. The most famous of these bells is the Liberty Bell, Fig. 5-18, used to announce the Declaration of Independence in Philadelphia. The reproduction of this bell, Fig. 5-19, may be used as a doorbell, dinner bell, or patio bell.

Fig. 5-18. Famous Cast Bronze **Liberty Bell,** Independence Hall, Philadelphia (Convention and Tourist Bureau Center)

Fig. 5-19. Cast Bell with Simulated Crack

Materials

Part	Pieces	Size	Suggested Materials
A — Bell	1	4'' dia. × 6''	Cast brass or aluminum
B — Yoke	1	2'' × 4''	White pine
C — Bracket	1	½'' × 3/16'' × 9''	Flat band iron
D — Axle	1	1/8'' × 8''	1/8'' dia. steel

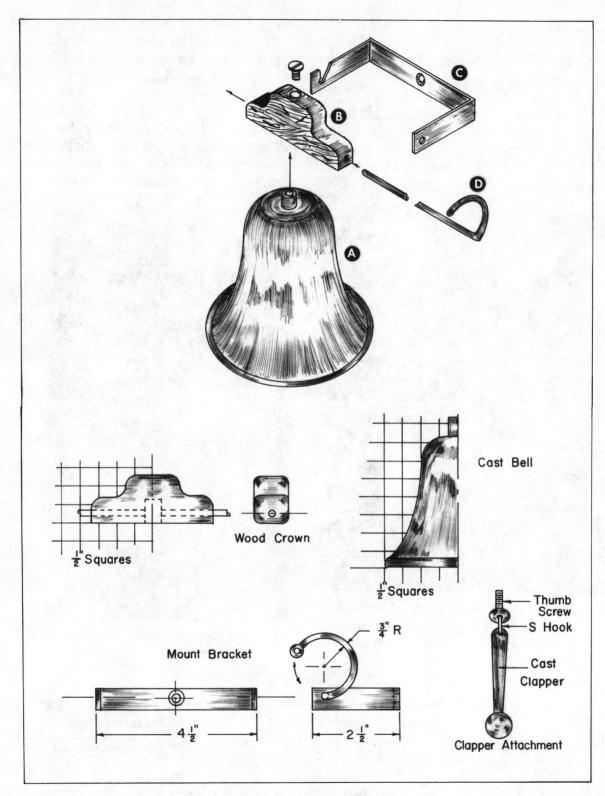

Cast Bell

Wood Crown

$\frac{1}{2}"$ Squares

$\frac{1}{2}"$ Squares

Mount Bracket

$\frac{3}{4}" R$

$4\frac{1}{2}"$

$2\frac{1}{2}"$

Thumb Screw

S Hook

Cast Clapper

Clapper Attachment

Fig. 5-20. Project Views of Cast Bell

Construction Procedure

Make a cast master from white pine in the shape suggested in Fig. 5-20. Follow standard foundry procedures when casting the bell.

PART A — BELL
Lathe turn the rough casting smooth.
Polish casting while it is on the lathe.
Drill and tap top center of the bell casting, $1/4'' - 20$.
Lathe turn one of the spruces to make a clapper.
Drill a $1/8''$ hole in the top of the clapper.

PART B — WOOD YOKE
Lay out suggested shape on white pine.
Cut out the stock and sand smooth. Distress.
Drill $1/8''$ hole lengthwise through yoke and $1/4''$ hole down through to match hole in bell.
Stain and lacquer wood yoke.

PART C — WALL BRACKET
Lay out and cut flat band stock to size.

Drill a $1/8''$ hole in each end, and countersink a $1/4''$ hole in dead center.
Bend the flat stock where directed in Fig. 5-20.
Cut a slot down to one of the $1/8''$ holes.

PART D — AXLE
Cut the $1/8''$ round stock to size.
Form a $2''$-diameter half-circle on one end, as shown. Then flatten the end.
Drill $\frac{1}{16}''$ hole in end of half circle.

FASTENING
Insert axle through wood yoke. Two ends of axle will fit in the $1/8''$ holes on the bracket. Bell is fastened to yoke with a $1/4''$ machine screw. Drill a $1/8''$ hole in the end of this machine screw and insert "S" hook through this hole and through hole in clapper.

Finish

The bell should be brightly polished ironwork, painted a flat black. For a special effect, paint a small crack on the bell with flat black paint, Fig. 5-19.

Fig. 5-21. Wrought Iron Doorlatch with Witch Mark (Salem Cross Inn, 1705)

Witch Mark Door Knocker

Superstitious colonists believed that witches or snakes would not cross ash wood to enter a household. Therefore, colonial doorways had ash thresholds as a means of hex control. Herbs, such as sage and dill, were supposed to restrain witches from performing evil tasks. Devices such as the cross on door latches, Fig. 5-21, were also a common means of "witch control." The Salem Cross Inn in West Brookfield, Massachusetts has several such latches. The reproduction, Fig. 5-22, serves as a door knocker for visitors other than so-called witches.

Materials

The best method for making this project is by casting. However, if casting material is not available, the knocker can be made from 33″ of ½″ × ¼″ mild bar steel.

Fig. 5-22. Witch Mark Door Knocker

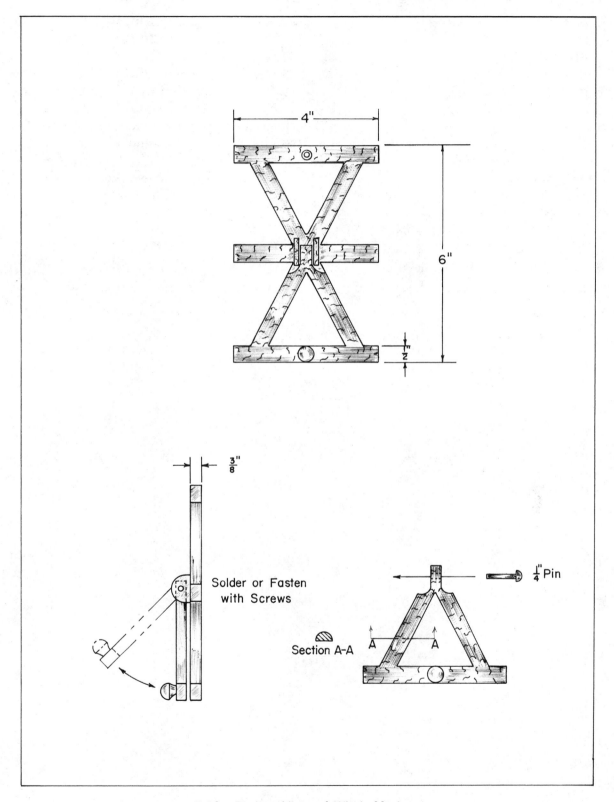

4"

6"

$\frac{1}{2}$"

$\frac{3}{8}$"

Solder or Fasten
with Screws

$\frac{1}{4}$" Pin

Section A-A

A   A

5-23. Project View of Witch Mark

Construction Procedure

Make a mold master from pine or other wood. Follow the design given in Fig. 5-23. The handle or knocker part is shaped to match the lower half of the design.

Follow standard foundry procedures for casting the parts.

File the casting smooth.

Peen the entire casting with a ball peen hammer.

Drill and countersink two $\frac{1}{4}''$ holes in the mark, and a $\frac{1}{8}''$ hole through both parts of the knocker holder.

Drill a $\frac{1}{8}''$ hole in the top of the knocker, and a tapped $\frac{1}{4}''$ hole in the bottom to receive the turned handle.

Lathe turn a small brass round to the handle shape and tap the shank end to fit the threaded hole in the knocker.

Fit a $\frac{1}{8}''$ pin through the $\frac{1}{8}''$ hole in the knocker and mark. Solder this pin to the mark only. The knocker should swing free on the pin.

Use flat head brass wood screws to fasten mark to door.

Finish

Wire brush the finished project and coat it with lacquer or paste wax.

Federal Eagle Door Knocker

In 1772 a traveling decorator paint-ed a large eagle on a house wall in Washington, Connecticut. This seems to have introduced the eagle as a symbol for freedom from English rule. Paper eagles were displayed in 1789 during Washington's tour of the new nation. Craftsmen, being quick to recognize its popularity, used this new symbol as a decorative figure for flagpole heads, ship sterns, customs houses, cloth, glass, buttons, and door knockers, Fig. 5-24.

No text on colonial metalwork would be complete without mention of a fed-eral eagle door knocker. A reproduction is shown in Fig. 5-25.

Materials

Project can be cast from brass or aluminum.

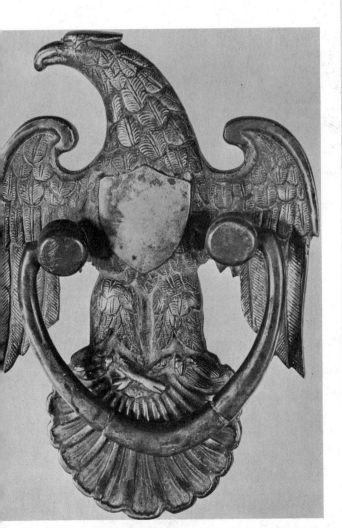

Fig. 5-24. Federal Eagle Door Knocker (Shel-burne Museum, Inc., E. J. Mengis)

Fig. 5-25. Cast Eagle Door Knocker

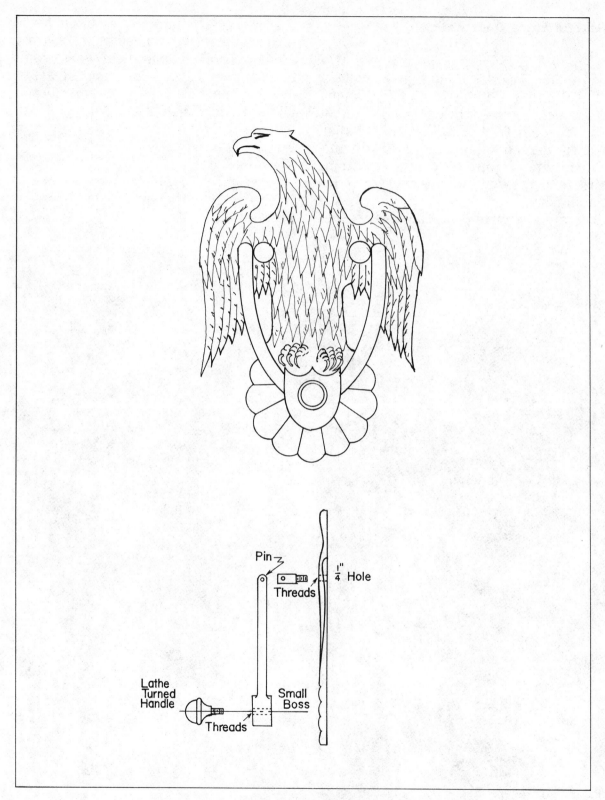

Fig. 5-26. Project Views of Cast Eagle Door Knocker

Construction Procedure

Make wooden mold masters of the eagle and knocker of ¼″ pine from 3″ to 7″ long. Feather detail, Fig 5-26, may be cut in with a small core box router bit or a V-chisel.

Follow standard foundry procedures for casting parts.

File the finished casting smooth, and sharpen feather details, if needed, with a grinder or half-round file.

Lathe turn two shoulders to receive the knocker. Create a ¼″ shank at bottom of shoulders and thread shanks.

Drill and tap two corresponding holes in the eagle to receive the shoulders.

Drill a ⅛″ hole in the tops of the shoulders to receive the swing pins.

Drill a ⅛″ hole in the top of the knocker to receive the pins.

Drill a ¼″ hole and thread it to receive the knob on the knocker, dead center on the bottom, Fig. 5-26.

Screw the shoulders into the eagle base.

Fasten the knocker to the shoulders by means of a ⅛″ brass pin on each side. Solder the pin to the knocker only. The knocker should swing free.

Screw the turned knob into the bottom of the knocker.

Fasten eagle to door with a flat-head brass wood screw.

Finish

Wire brush the finished project and coat it with lacquer or paste wax.

UNIT 6

Yankee Tin

Tin was used for common household articles. Although expensive, it was much lighter than iron. In 1738 Edgar Patterson opened the first tin shop in Berlin, Connecticut. He made tin plates, cups, lanterns, candle sconces, and other tinware which sold as fast as he could make them. After his market in Berlin was saturated, he sent his products to outlying towns. Eventually tinware was known all over New England.

In milder weather peddlers traveled the countryside selling the products that tinsmiths had made during the winter. Peddlers often covered 1,500 miles in one season.

In 1791 Paul Revere imported a collection of japanned or Roman painted tin, which added new beauty to plain tin and also protected it from rusting, Fig. 6-1.

The reproductions offered in this section are examples of tinware and light-gage steel flatware. Some are composites of early pieces, while others are exact reproductions.

Fig. 6-1.   Hand-Painted Yankee Tin Kettle and Cup (Shelburne Museum, Inc., E. J. Mengis)

84

Candle Mold

Sconces in colonial homes held hand-made candles which were made by either dipping or molding. The mold method was very common because several candles could be poured at the same time. Also, they were easier to make than hand-dipped tapers, Fig. 2-1.

To fill the needs of the housewives, tinsmiths made candle molds in abundance. Today, however, genuine molds, such as the one shown in Fig. 6-2, are hard to find; if found, they are in poor condition.

Reproductions of colonial candle molds are useful as wall decorations, Fig. 6-3, or lamp motifs. The molds, of course, may also be used to make your own candles.

Fig. 6-2. Candle Molds (Shelburne Museum, E. J. Mengis)

Fig. 6-3. Candle Molds Used as Wall Motif

Materials

Part	Pieces	Size	Suggested Materials
A — Top pan	1	4" × 6 ½"	Sheet copper, brass, sheet metal
B — Bottom pan	1	4" × 6 ½"	Sheet copper, brass, sheet metal
C — Tapers	8	3" × 10"	Sheet copper, brass, sheet metal

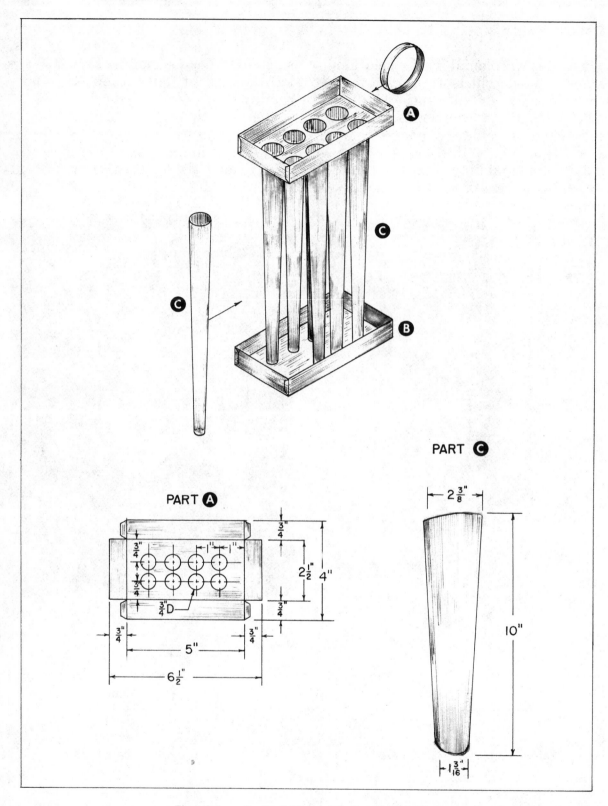

Fig. 6-4.   Project Views of Candle Mold

Construction Procedure

Lay out required shapes on metal and cut out.

PART A — TOP PAN

Punch or cut eight ¾" holes evenly spaced in the pan, as shown in Fig. 6-4.

Form a simple hem* on all four edges.

Bend the sides up at right angles to form the pan.

Solder the corners together.

Solder a finger ring to one end.

PART B — BOTTOM PAN

Punch or drill eight ⅛" holes corresponding with the ¾" holes in the top pan.

Form a simple hem* on all four sides.

Bend the hemmed sides up at right angles to the pan.

Solder the corners together.

PART C — TAPERS

Lay out a paper pattern first to determine shape.

Transfer the paper pattern to eight pieces of stock.

Form into taper tubes with a simple lap seam.

Solder the lap seams tight and smooth.

FASTENING

Fit the eight taper tubes into the ¾" holes in the top pan.

Fillet-solder the tapers to the pan, flush with the top.

Center the bottom of the tapers over the ⅛" holes in the bottom pan and fillet-solder.

*A wire edge may be used in place of a hem.

Finish

All metal should be bright; brass, bronze or copper needs only to be steel-wooled to a high sheen. Sheet metal should be sanded and then steel-wooled to look like English pewter. No paint is necessary.

Candlemaking

Insert a cotton wick with a knotted end through each of the ⅛" holes.

Secure the wick in the center of each tube top by tying it to ⅛" rods laid across the tubes.

Melt the wax and pour it into the tube holes. (Wax may be colored by melting crayons in with it.)

Cut off the knot when the wax solidifies.

Heat the outside of the mold slightly, and candles will drop out.

Pierced Lantern

The origin of this lantern is uncertain, as it is difficult to establish the true age of authentic pieces. Sometimes these lanterns are called "Paul Revere lamps," since some historians claim this type of lamp was used the night of his famous ride. Other historians claim that Paul Revere made such lamps in his copper shop, thus the reason for the name.

This lamp has a very short field of illumination, but because only a very strong wind can blow out the candle, these lanterns were very popular among colonists as "carry lights."

The New York Metropolitan Museum and the Brewster Collection in Springfield Museum have two very old pierced lanterns, Figs. 6-5 and 6-10. A reproduction is shown in Fig. 6-6.

Fig. 6-5.　Pierced Lantern (Metropolitan Museum of Art)

This tin lantern with conical top is 15" high. The numerous holes permitted light from the candle to stream through.

Materials

Part	Pieces	Size	Suggested Materials
A — Body	1	8 ½" × 16"	Tin plate, brass, copper
Door	1	4" × 4"	or 28-gage sheet metal
B — Bottom	1	5" dia.	Same
Candle socket	1	¾" dia.	Same
C — Top cone	1	7" × 11"	Same
D — Baffle	1	3" × 5"	Same
E — Hand ring	1	1/8" × 7"	1/8" brass round

Fig. 6-6.   Pierced Lantern Reproduction

Construction Procedure

Make a full-size development of all the parts.

Lay out a design for piercing. See Figs. 6-7 and 6-8.

Tape the paper patterns to the inside of the stock.

Cut out the stock along lines given in the pattern.

Punch out the design in all the parts from the inside out, Fig. 6-9, using a sharp awl or nail, and a wood butt chisel.

PART A — BODY

Lay out and cut a 3″ × 3″ door opening in the stock.

Form a simple lock seam on each end.

Form body into a cylinder on a slip roll.

Solder the lock seam.

Roll-bead the bottom edge to receive the bottom Part B.

DOOR

Cut out 4″ × 4″ stock.

Match the design from the body and punch out.

Shape the door on a slip roll to match body contour.

Solder on a small pair of hinges and a hasp.

Center over opening in Part A and solder hinges in place.

PART B — BOTTOM

Fit 5″ diameter circle to fit inside roll bead on Part A.

Solder ¾″ diameter candle socket in center.

Solder bottom into bead on Part A.

PART C — CONE

Form a cone from prepierced stock.

Make a simple lap seam in the cone.

Solder the lap seam.

Roll-bead the bottom edge of the cone so that it fits over and around Part A.

Solder the cone to Part A.

PART D — BAFFLE

Form Part D the same as Part C.

Drill or punch two ⅛″ holes ½″ from the apex to hold hand ring.

Drill or punch matching holes in Part C apex.

PART E — HAND RING

Form a ring from ⅛″ brass round.

Insert through holes in Parts C and D. Solder ends.

Finish

Tin plate, brass or copper lanterns have bright finishes, Fig. 6-6. Sheet metal may be burnished to look like pewter or painted in pewter tone, bronze, or flat black.

Fig. 6-7.   Daisy Ornamental Pattern

Fig. 6-8.   Sunburst Ornamental Pattern

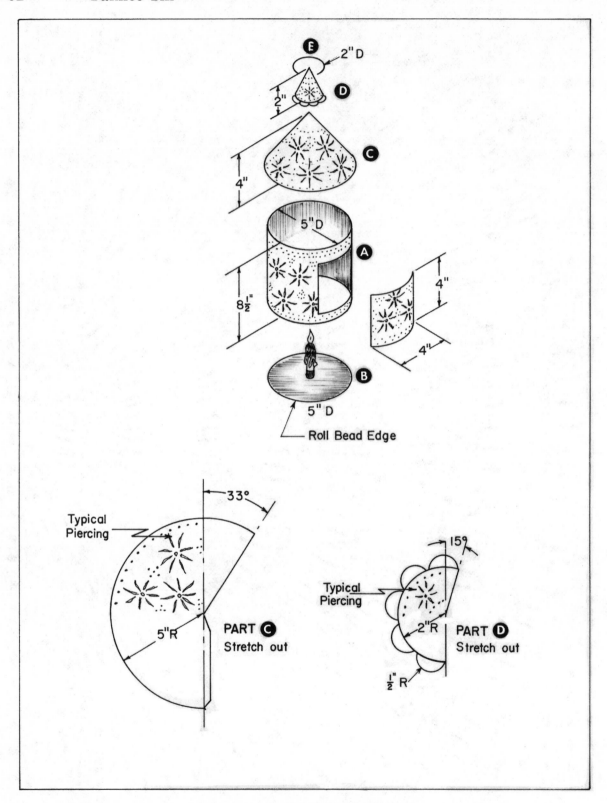

Fig. 6-9.   Project Views of Pierced Lantern

Tinker's Sconce

Tinkers made sconces mainly as a side line. As "carry around" lights, these sconces were adequate for barn work and general lighting, Fig. 6-10. The mirror provided reflection of the single candle beam, and the high-peaked top shielded the carrier's hand from the heat of the flame.

Sconces by the thousands were sold to colonists in New England by the traveling tinkers, but now only a few remain. Farmers liked these sconces because the enclosed flame offered some protection against fire in the out-buildings.

The basic size, design and construction of the reproduction in Fig. 6-10 was taken from a sconce in the Springfield Museum.

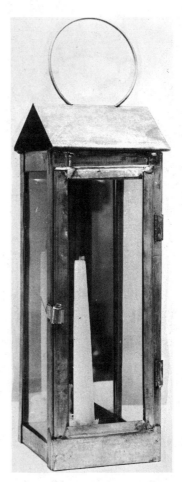

Fig. 6-10. Early Sconce (Springfield Museum, Mass., Brewster Collection)

Materials

Part	Pieces	Size	Suggested Materials
A — Pans	2	6" × 6"	Tin plate, brass or 22-gage sheet metal
Candle socket	1	¾" dia.	Same
B — Front rails	2	1" × 12"	Same
Backpiece	1	6" × 12"	Same
C — Door rails	2	½" × 11"	Same
	2	½" × 4 ¼"	Same
D — Roof	1	5" × 7 ½"	Same
Hand ring	1	1/8" × 14"	1/8" brass round
Glass clips	8	1" × 4"	Scrap stock
Glass	2	4 ¼" × 11 ½"	Single strength
	1	3 ¼" × 10"	Single strength
Mirror	1	4 ¼" × 11 ½"	Single strength

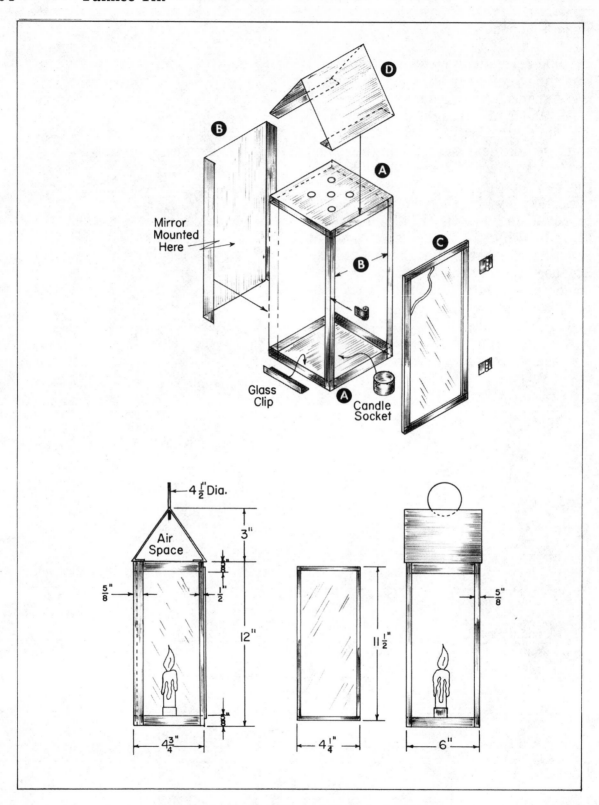

Fig. 6-11. Project Views of Tinker's Sconce

Construction Procedure

Lay out all sizes required on material selected for sconce, Fig. 6-11, allowing for seams.

Cut out the stock and file all cuts smooth.

PART A — PANS
Bend the ⅝" sides up on a pan break to form a box.

Drill ⅛" ventilation holes in pan to be used on top.

Solder the corners of the pans.

Solder a standard candle socket to center of bottom pan.

PART B — FRONT RAILS
Bend the rails in half lengthwise to form right angles.

Solder front rails to both pans, keeping work square.

BACK PIECE
Bend the edges of the back side to form right angles.

Solder the back side to pans, keeping work square.

PART C — DOOR RAILS
Bend the rails to a U-shape on a bar fold or break, referring to details on Fig. 6-11.

Miter the corners of the rails to form rectangle.

Solder the two sides and the top together, keeping the U-channel free of solder.

Insert single strength glass into the door and solder on bottom piece.

Solder on hinges and hasp.

PART D — ROOF
Bend the stock to match the angle shown in Fig. 6-11.

Allow a ½" seam or bend on each end. The roof will overhang ¼" all around.

Drill or punch the roof to take a ⅛" hand ring.

Solder roof to the top pan.

Insert hand ring through holes and solder.

GLASS CLIPS
Make glass clips from scrap stock, shaping them into simple right angles.

Solder the top clips in place, allowing for the thickness of the glass and mirror.

Install the precut glass and mirror into the sconce.

Solder the lower clips in place.

NOTE: This lamp may be wired for an electric candle if so desired. See Fig. 6-14 for details.

Finish

Sheet metal requires buffing to achieve a pewterlike effect; lacquer after buffing. The lamp can be painted in any special tone or flat black. Tin plate needs no finish.

Wentworth Sconce

The Wentworth sconce, Fig. 6-12, was named after a governor of New Hampshire. A sconce similar to the reproduction shown here now hangs in the central hallway of the Governor Wentworth home in Portsmouth.

Colored glass or leaded glass may be used in this sconce which is suitable for patio or house lighting, Fig. 6-13.

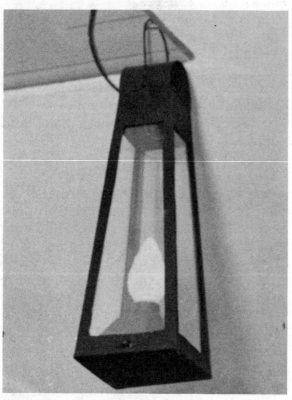

Fig. 6-12. Wentworth Hall Sconce (Wentworth House, Old Portsmouth, N. H.)

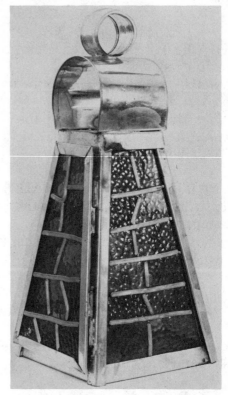

Fig. 6-13. Wentworth Sconce with Stained Glass

Materials

Part	Pieces	Size	Suggested Materials
A — Pans (Top)	1	4 ½" × 4 ½"	Tin plate, brass or
(Bottom)	1	7 ¼" × 7 ¼"	24-gage sheet metal
Candle socket	1	¾" dia.	24-gage sheet metal
B — Rails	4	1" × 9"	24-gage sheet metal
C — Door Rails	2	1" × 8"	24-gage sheet metal
	2	1" × 6 ½"	24-gage sheet metal
D — Roof	1	4" × 8"	24-gage sheet metal
Hand ring	1	¾" × 9"	24-gage sheet metal
Glass	4	7" × 9"	Single strength window glass or colored glass

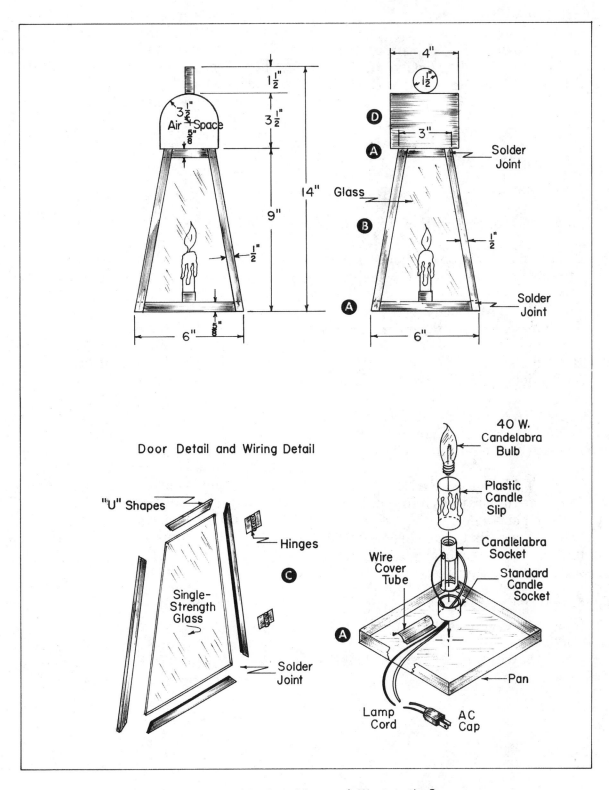

Door Detail and Wiring Detail

Fig. 6-14. Project Views of Wentworth Sconce

Construction Procedure

Cut all stock to the size suggested in Fig. 6-14. A ⅛″ hardboard template will help in construction of the angles.

PART A — PANS
TOP
File all edges smooth and mark for bends.

Bend the sides up to form right angle.

Solder the ends together to form a box.

Drill small crisscross holes across top to permit candle heat to escape.

BOTTOM
File all edges smooth and mark for bends.

Bend the sides up.

Solder joints together to form a box.

CANDLE SOCKET
Solder a standard candle socket to the center of the bottom piece.

PART B — RAILS
Bend the four rails in half lengthwise to form right angles.

Solder the rails to the corners of the pans. Use the hardboard template to maintain correct angles.

PART C — DOOR RAILS
Check door construction in Fig. 6-14 for details.

Bend the rails in a U-shape lengthwise.

Miter the corners to form angles required.

Solder the two sides and the top together, keeping the inside of the "U" free of solder.

Insert single-strength window glass into frame and solder on the bottom piece.

Solder a pair of small hinges and a hasp to door.

PART D — ROOF
Bend the roof stock to shape shown in Fig. 6-14.

Solder roof to the top pan.

Drill or punch roof to take ⅛″ hand ring.

HAND RING
Cut ⅛″ brass or steel round to size.

Form into circle on a slip roll.

Insert through roof holes and solder the two ends of the ring together.

GLASS CLIPS
Make eight glass clips to accommodate sizes shown in Fig. 6-14.

Solder the lower clips in place on the bottom pan, using the ⅛″ hardboard template as a spacer.

Insert the glass and solder the top clips in place.

Finish

Tin plate, sheet brass, or copper should be natural. Sheet metal may be buffed to resemble pewter or painted in any special tone or solid color.

Scale

Scales, introduced in the colonies in the early 18th century, were used as weight measures in all colonial shops and most households. Originally, they were very simple devices, made to be held by hand or hung from a wall or shelf, Fig. 6-15A. Refinements appeared later when balance scales became free standing and had heavy bases of wood or marble, Fig. 6-15B.

A modern reproduction of these old wrought iron scales can be used as a table centerpiece or as end table decor, Fig. 6-16 and 6-17.

(A) Early balance scale mounted on a shelf. (Old Sturbridge Village, Mass.)

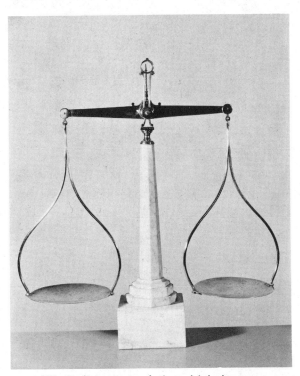

(B) Refinement of the old balance scale using a marble base (Henry Francis duPont Winterthur Museum)

Fig. 6-15. Balance Scales

Materials

Part	Pieces	Size	Suggested Materials
A — Main stem	1	3/8" × 16 1/2"	1/8" flat band stock
Eagle	1	2 1/4"	Brass lamp finial
Pin Finial	1	1/2" × 1 1/2"	Brass round
B — Balance arm	1	3/8" × 20"	1/8" flat band stock
C — Support	1	3/8" × 26"	1/8" flat band stock
D — Base	1	1" × 7" dia.	Pine or similar wood
E — Dishes	2	6" dia.	Brass or pine
Chain	6	9" long	#20 brass chain

Fig. 6-16. Balance Scale with Eagle Finial, Scroll Stem, and Wood Base

Construction Procedure

Cut the flat band stock and file all ends smooth.

PART A — MAIN STEM

Split the main stem piece $1\frac{1}{2}''$ at the bottom.

Heat and form the split into scroll loops.

Mark out where twists will occur in stem, Fig. 6-18. (Twists in stem are made at places along stem where they will not interfere when Parts B and C are joined to stem.)

Heat and twist the piece with an adjustable wrench where marked.

Reheat and draw the top into a $\frac{1}{4}''$ diameter round.

Drill a $\frac{3}{16}''$ hole in stem for the swing pin.

Thread the $\frac{1}{4}''$ round top to receive the brass finial.

EAGLE FINIAL

Eagle lamp finials are available in most hardware stores and are threaded for a $\frac{1}{4}''$ threaded shaft.

PIN FINIAL

Lathe turn a piece of brass round to suggested shape.

Drill a $\frac{3}{16}''$ hole part way through the finial and tap it to match a $\frac{3}{16}''$ machine screw.

PART B — BALANCE ARM

Lay out a full scale drawing of this arm, using French curves.

Drill a $\frac{3}{16}''$ hole dead center, and a $\frac{1}{8}''$ hole $\frac{1}{2}''$ in from each end.

Heat and shape the balance arm to match the drawing.

Reheat and make the twists suggested in Fig. 6-19.

Attach balance arm to stem with a machine screw and finial.

PART C — SUPPORT

Heat and shape the support piece into a large loop with reverse scroll ends. (See Appendix, Section I for curve and scroll details.)

Weld the support on dead center to the main stem where the scrolls meet at the bottom.

Weld a headless $\frac{1}{4}''$ bolt to the bottom.

PART D — BASE

Cut a $7''$ diameter circle from $2''$ pine or similar wood.

Lathe turn the base to desired shape.

Drill a $\frac{1}{4}''$ hole dead center and counterbore it $1''$ wide, $\frac{3}{4}''$ deep.

Sand and finish the base according to suggestions below. Felt the bottom, cutting out hole around the counterbore.

Secure the main stem to the base, using a $1''$ washer and nut on the welded bolt.

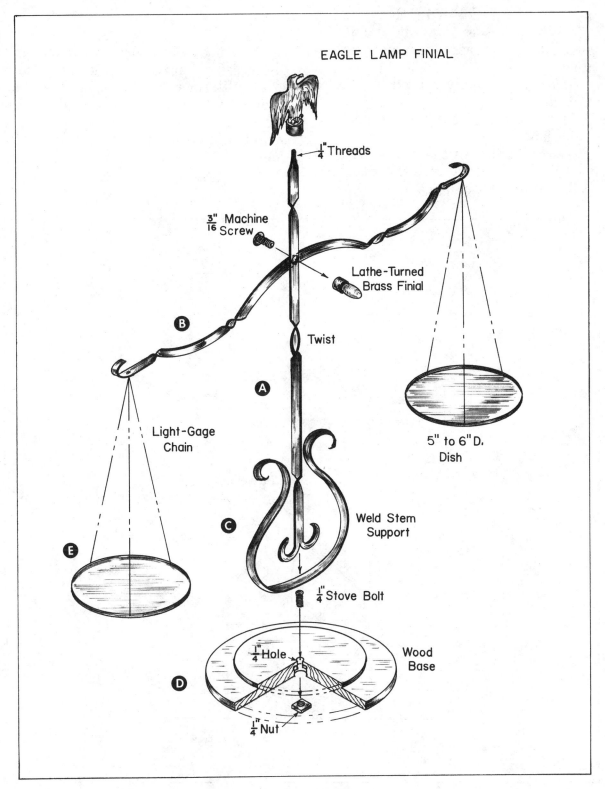

EAGLE LAMP FINIAL

$\frac{1}{4}$" Threads

$\frac{3}{16}$" Machine Screw

Lathe-Turned Brass Finial

B

Twist

A

Light-Gage Chain

5" to 6" D. Dish

C

Weld Stem Support

E

$\frac{1}{4}$" Stove Bolt

$\frac{1}{4}$" Hole

Wood Base

D

$\frac{1}{4}$" Nut

Fig. 6-17. Project Views of Balance Scale

PART E — DISHES

The two dishes may be made by lathe-spinning brass stock, or by lathe-turning wood.

Drill three equally spaced, ⅛" holes in each dish.

Attach three pieces of #20 chain to each dish.

Secure the tops of the chains with an open link and then secure the open link to the end of the balance arm.

Finish

The wood scale base is sanded and distressed. Apply a dark stain and cover with several coats of lacquer. The wrought iron is buffed and coated with brushing lacquer. Brass work is kept bright and covered with brushing lacquer.

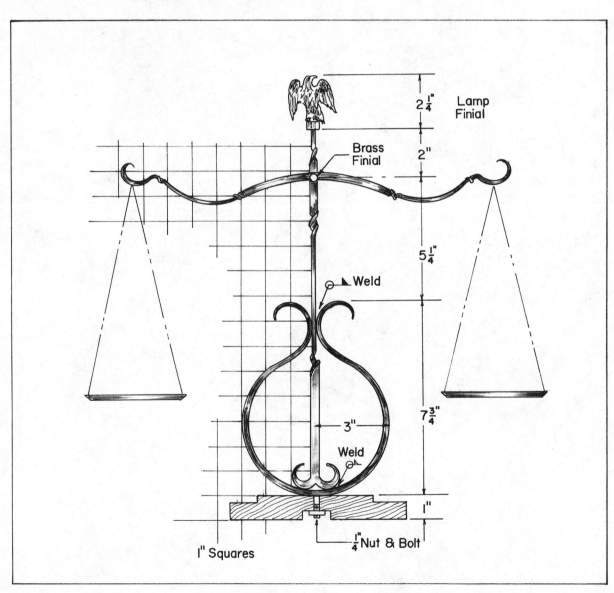

Fig. 6-18. Construction Details for Balance Scale

Drum Wastebasket

The side drum is associated with the birth of freedom. The regimental drummer boy from town or hamlet who went with his company in battle against the Redcoats is immortalized in the famous painting, "The Spirit of '76."

Drums used in the Revolutionary War were decorated with sunbursts, slogans, town mottos, eagles, and bright colors or flags, Fig. 6-19. They represented each colony which took pride in the fact that it was doing its best for the cause of freedom.

Colonial Williamsburg, West Point, and Guilford Museum have some of the best collections of these early American and English battle drums, Fig. 6-20.

The reproduction, Fig. 6-21, adapted from these museum pieces, may be constructed and painted as a drum, but used as a wastebasket.

Fig. 6-19. Colonial Regimental Drum (Guilford Courthouse Museum)

Fig. 6-20. English Regimental Kettle Drum from the Battle of Saratoga, 1777 (West Point Museum)

Materials

Part	Pieces	Size	Suggested Materials
A — Upper rim	1	3" × 34"	28-gage sheet metal
Lower rim	1	3" × 34"	28-gage sheet metal
B — Trunk	1	14" × 36"	28-gage sheet metal
C — Bottom	1	10" dia.	28-gage sheet metal
D — Ties	8	1" × 3"	Leather straps, discarded
E — Rope	1	8 ft. long	belts or leather shoestrings ¼" nylon cord

Fig. 6-21. Side Drum Reproduction

Construction Procedure

Lay out and cut all required parts. File the edges smooth.

PART A — RIMS

Bend and shape the two rims as suggested in Fig. 6-22.

Form into a circle using a slip roll. (The bends may have to be reopened after slip rolling.)

Solder the joints and file smooth.

Drill eight evenly spaced, $\frac{1}{4}''$ holes along each rim lip as shown.

PART B — TRUNK

Make a wave lap seam. (Do not complete the seam until after the trunk is inserted into the rims.)

Insert the trunk into the top and lower rims. The lower rim should be turned until the holes are at midpoint between the holes in the top rim.

Complete the wave lap seam by soldering and riveting.

PART C — BOTTOM

Cut a 10'' diameter circle and mark for a $\frac{1}{4}''$ burr edge.

Roll-bead the circumference to form right angle or burr edge.

Force-fit the bottom into the trunk so that the burr edge slips into the inside lip on the lower rim.

Solder the trunk, bottom, and lower rim together. The top rim may be soldered if desired.

Paint the drum at this point. (See finishing details.)

PART D — LEATHER TIES

Cut out eight leather ties in the shape suggested in Fig. 6-22.

Punch or cut holes in the ties.

Insert one tie for each set of holes in the lace work.

PART E — ROPE

Thread the rope through a lower hole, bringing rope up through the hole in a leather tie, through a hole in the top rim, over the rim and back through the hole in the leather tie, then through another hole in the lower rim, and so on until the entire drum is laced.

Pull the cord tight with all the leather ties up near the top rim and tie off the cord at the bottom. (Pulling the leather ties down will take out any slack in the rope cord.)

Finish

Paint the drum as desired in bright colors and apply large eagle decals, school mascots or state flags to the trunk sides. For authentic effect, add a pair of drum sticks which may be lathe-turned or shaped with a draw knife. Apply dark stain or black paint to sticks.

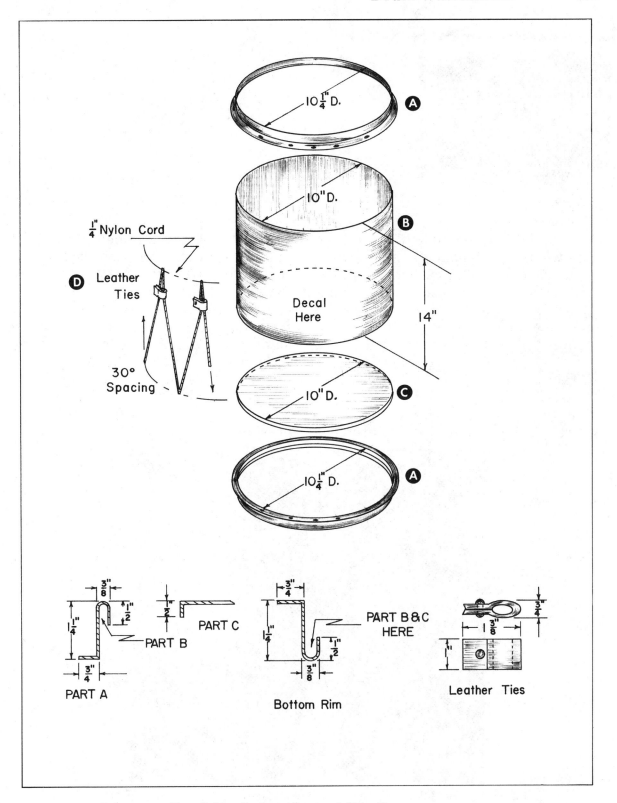

Fig. 6-22. Project Views of Side Drum

Lamplight

Lamplight is reminiscent of the old inns where large chandeliers hung over groups of colonists discussing the pressing problem of English taxes. Lamplight from these chandeliers was a sign of welcome to travelers who stopped at these taverns for food, drink, and a night's lodging.

The "Sons of Liberty," meeting at the Raleigh Tavern, Fig. 7-1, drank rum and made speeches on independence. The Buckman Tavern provided the meeting place for the Minute Men, and the Wayside Inn was the scene of reassembly after the Battle of Lexington.

The chandeliers in these taverns and inns were almost as popular as the signboards. The reproduction of the Raleigh chandelier is an exact replica of the original which still hangs in the taproom of that tavern. The wayside chandelier is a composite of some general tavern lighting.

Fig. 7-1. Note the Raleigh Chandelier Located in the Raleigh Taproom (Colonial Williamsburg)

Raleigh Chandelier

Chandeliers of this type used in the Raleigh Tavern, Fig. 7-2, lighted many taprooms and taverns, and can be identified by the several candle arms reaching out in all directions from a center base. In the Raleigh Tavern and the Deerfield Tavern hang two of the oldest multi-arm chandeliers.

The reproduction, (Fig. 7-3), copies the early 18th century museum pieces. The chandelier is wired for electric socket-type bulbs, but otherwise the details are the same as the old lamps still hanging in famous taverns. See Fig. 7-4 and 7-5.

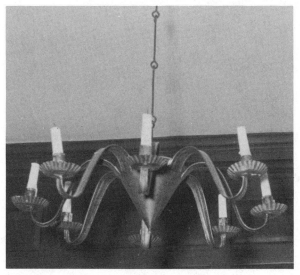

Fig. 7-2.   Closeup of Raleigh Chandelier (Colonial Williamsburg)

Fig. 7-3.   Raleigh Chandelier

Materials

Part	Pieces	Size	Suggested Materials
A — Cones	1	6'' dia. circle	26-gage sheet metal
	1	8'' dia. circle	26-gage sheet metal
B — Rod	1	10'' long	1/8'' I.P.S.
Finials	2	¾'' × 3''	¾'' brass round
C — Candle arms	6	2'' × 14''	26-gage sheet metal
Dishes	6	2 ½'' dia.	26-gage sheet metal
Sockets	6	¾'' dia.	26-gage sheet metal
D — Electric parts	6	110-volt	Electric sockets
	6	¾'' × 6''	Plastic covers
	6	40-watt	Flame Tip® bulbs
	1	20''	Link chain
	1	20'	Lamp cord
	1	110-volt	Outlet box cover
	1	2-prong	A.C. cap

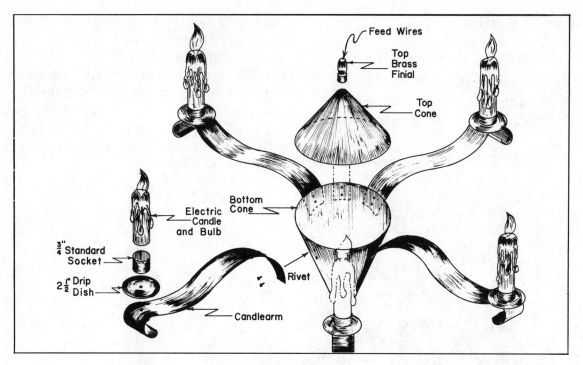

Fig. 7-4.   Isometrical View of Raleigh Chandelier

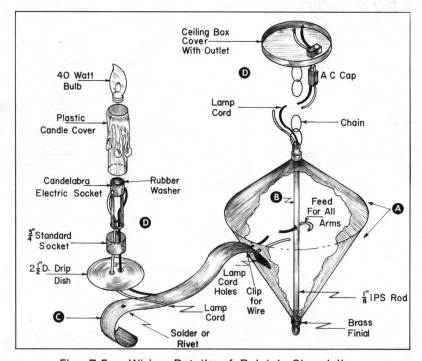

Fig. 7-5.   Wiring Details of Raleigh Chandelier

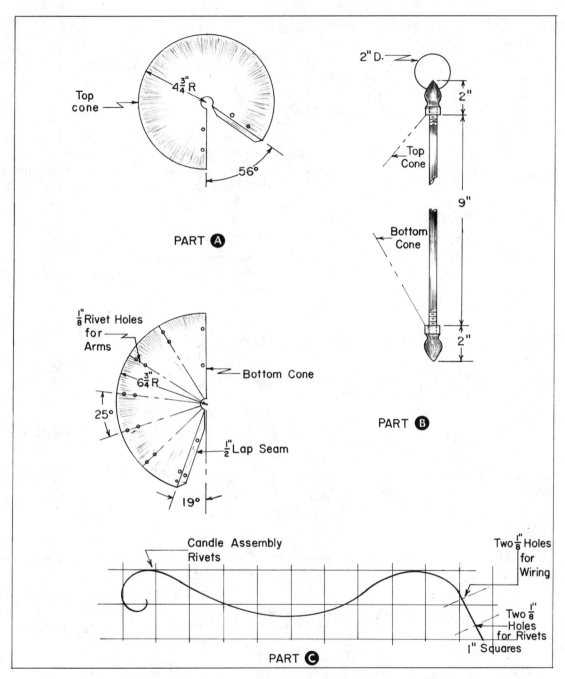

Fig. 7-6.   Cone and Arm Construction Details for the Raleigh Chandelier

Construction Procedure

PART A — CONES

Lay out paper stretch-outs of the cones, Fig. 7-6.

Transfer paper pattern to metal and cut out. File smooth.

Punch or drill ⅛″ rivet holes for six evenly spaced arms in the lower cone only.

Shape both cones on a slip roll or blowhorn stake.

Rivet and solder the lap seams on both cones.

Roll-bead the circumference of the top cone so that, after wiring, it can be fitted over lower cone tightly.

Cut off the tips of each cone so the ⅛″ IPS rod clears freely.

PART B — IPS ROD

Drill a 3/16″ hole in the center of the rod.

FINIALS

Lathe turn two brass finials shown in Fig. 7-5 and 7-6.

Drill and tap both finials with ⅛″ IPS thread.

Drill through 3/16″ hole in top finial for electric feed.

Drill ⅛″ cross hole in top finial for ring.

Secure top finial to rod and feed wire through finial and rod to exit from pre-drilled 3/16″ hole.

PART C — CANDLE ARMS

Cut and file stock for six candle arms, Fig. 7-5 and 7-6.

Roll-bead both edges with large bead.

Insert lamp cord in each bead and close bead carefully.

NOTE: Allow enough excess of lamp cord on each end to make splice and wire electric sockets.

Shape each arm on a slip roll. Wire inserts will shape with the metal.

Mark and punch or drill two ⅛″ rivet holes on each arm where it joins the cone.

Rivet the wired assembly to the lower cone.

Solder a candle dish and socket to the end of each arm.

NOTE: Candle dishes are drilled so wires can be fed through center.

LAMP WIRING DETAIL

Feed the lamp cord down through the top finial, through the ⅛″ IPS rod and out the 3/16″ holes in center as shown in Fig. 7-5.

Tie an underwriter's knot on each set of wires from the candle arms as it enters the lower cone.

Connect the sets of wires from the candle arms with two wires from IPS rod by making a six-way solder splice.

Interrupt the black wire if a switch is required. It may be placed on the side of the lower cone.

Fasten the two cones together. The two finials and ⅛″ IPS rod are fastened as a nut and bolt.

String the wire up the chain to an AC two-prong cap.

Solder an adjustable electric socket at the end of the candle arms.

Feed wire up the adjustable socket and secure to screws.

Insert plastic covers over adjustable sockets.

Insert a 40-watt bulb in each adjustable socket.

HOUSEHOLD WIRING DETAIL

Attach a ceiling outlet box cover with a hook and female outlet to electrical supply outlet.

Attach the lamp chain to the outlet box cover.

Plug the AC cap into the female outlet on the cover.

Finish

The complete lamp is painted flat black, except the brass finials which should be polished. Wax may be dripped on the plastic candle covers for a more authentic appearance.

Wayside Chandelier

This chandelier is a composite replica of many types of colonial chandeliers, Fig. 7-7. Its distressed pine base, hand-wrought iron candle base, and deep candle arms are representative of many different styles of chandeliers found in restoration settlements. The wagon wheel chandelier evolved from such a basic form.

Fig. 7-7. Wayside Chandelier

Materials

Part	Pieces	Size	Suggested Materials
A — Plank	1	5″ × 26″	2″ white pine
B — Candle base	2	1 ¼″ × 29″	3/16″ flat band stock
C — Candle arms	6	1″ × 10″	Aluminum round pipe
D — Arm brackets	6	1 ¼″ × 3 ½″	3/16″ flat band stock
E — Arm finials	6	1″ dia.	2″ aluminum round
Accessories			
Drip dish	6	2″ dia.	26-gage sheet metal
Sockets	6	¾″ dia.	26-gage sheet metal
Threaded rod	6	3/8′ × 3″	1/8″ I.P.S.
Lock nuts	6	½″	1/8″ I.P.S.
Bolts	2	3/8″ × 3″	Square head with nut
Eye bolts	2	1″ dia.	¼″ screw eye
Electrical parts			
Socket base	6	¾″ × 6″	Adjustable candelabra
Candle covers	6	¾″ × 6″	Plastic
Bulbs	6	40-watt	Flame Tip®
Lamp cord	1	20′	Lamp cord wire
Chain	1	26″	Chandelier chain
Outlet cover	1	110-volt	Ceiling plate
Cap	1	2-prong	A.C. cap
Rubber grommet	6	3/8″ dia.	Electric grommets

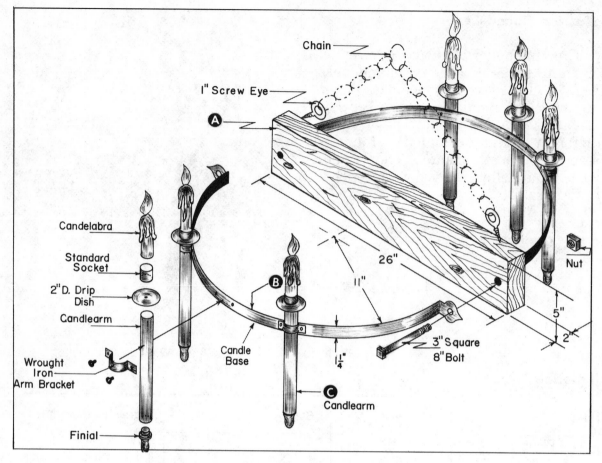

Fig. 7-8.   Project View of Wayside Chandelier

Construction Procedure

PART A — PLANK

Cut wood stock to size and sand edges smooth and rounded. See finishing details.

Drill a ⅜″ hole dead center at 2 ½″ from each end. The half-circle candle bases will be fastened to the plank with ⅜″ bolts in these holes.

Drill a ¼″ entrance hole for electric wire approximately ½″ inside the ⅜″ holes. The lamp cord will enter from the candle arms through these holes.

Drill screw eye holes in top as shown in Fig. 7-8.

Drill ¼″ entrance holes for wire near screw eye hole, down to meet ¼″ cross-drilled holes.

PART B — CANDLE BASE

Cut and file two pieces of 1 ¼″ flat band stock to size.

Heat and spear-point both ends of each piece.

Reheat and shape these two pieces into half circles.

Bend spear points out at right angles for mounting to plank. The rings should match each other.

Drill ⅜″ hole in center of each spear point.

Mark the location of candles as they are to be fastened to candle base.

Mark out and drill $\frac{5}{16}''$ wire feed holes behind and between rivet holes for arm brackets.

PART C — CANDLE ARMS

Cut and file six pieces of 1″ aluminum pipe 10″ long for candle arms.

Force-fit Part E (finials) into bottoms of candle arms.

PART D — ARM BRACKETS

Cut and file six pieces of flat band stock for brackets.

Heat and shape the brackets around the candle arms for a close fit to candle base, allowing a flange end on each side of bracket, Fig. 7-8. The shape of the arm brackets will vary, so each one should be numbered and marked individually.

Drill a $\frac{1}{4}''$ rivet hole in each flange end. Transfer these holes to the candle base, mark and drill.

ASSEMBLY

Place a candle arm in the arm bracket, Part D. Allow 2″ of the pipe to extend above the bracket. Rivet the bracket to Part B, the candle base; the candle arms should be securely held in place.

After all six arms are in place, loosely bolt each candle base to sides of the plank until feed is completed. Insert screw eyes and chain.

After electrical feed is finished, bolt the rings to the plank tightly.

CANDLE ARM WIRING

Lathe turn six pieces of hardwood to fit inside the candle arms.

Drill a $\frac{3}{8}''$ hole through center of the wood.

Insert a piece of $\frac{1}{8}''$ IPS rod through the hole; attach a lock nut to the bottom.

Insert a premade candle drip dish and candle socket over the pipe.

Screw an adjustable candelabra socket to top of threaded rod. The screw effect of the adjustable socket and lock nut will hold the assembly together.

Force-fit the assembly into the top of the candle arm after the adjustable socket is wired.

Install the plastic candle cover and 40-watt bulb, Fig. 7-9.

MAIN FEED WIRING

Feed the lamp cord down the chandelier chain, through the holes in the plank to the first candle arm.

Feed through the arm up to the first candelabra adjustable socket.

Wire the socket and return the feed out from the candle arm over to the next candle arm until all six arms are wired.

Wire can be held close to the candle base with sheet metal wrap-around clips.

Allow a few inches slack at the top of the chain and attach a 2-prong AC cap.

Attach a ceiling outlet box cover with a hook and female outlet.

Hook the chandelier chain to the outlet hook and insert the AC cap into the outlet.

Finish

Paint all metal flat black. Distress the wood plank and stain, and apply several coats of lacquer. Melted wax may be dripped over the plastic candle covers and drip dishes for authentic effect, if desired.

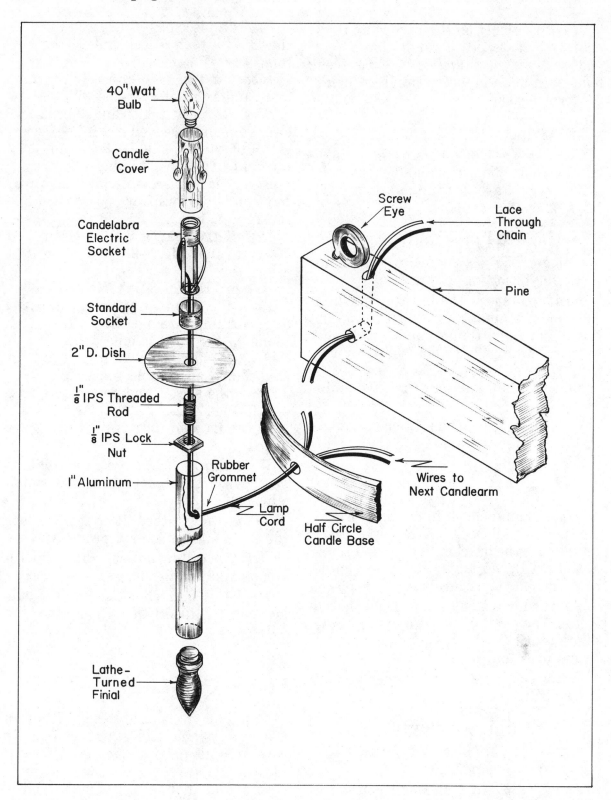

40" Watt Bulb

Candle Cover

Candelabra Electric Socket

Standard Socket

2" D. Dish

$\frac{1}{8}$" IPS Threaded Rod

$\frac{1}{8}$" IPS Lock Nut

1" Aluminum

Rubber Grommet

Lamp Cord

Half Circle Candle Base

Lathe-Turned Finial

Screw Eye

Lace Through Chain

Pine

Wires to Next Candlearm

Fig. 7-9.   Wiring Details for Wayside Chandelier

Friendship Lamp

The friendship sconce originated in the Dutch region of Pennsylvania. The colonists adopted the heart shape as one on their basic designs which appeared in such forms as tool handles, (Fig. 3-2), candle backs, (Fig. 7-10), samplers, and even on birth certificates.

This reproduction is an electric wall fixture and will enhance any wall or corner, Fig. 7-11.

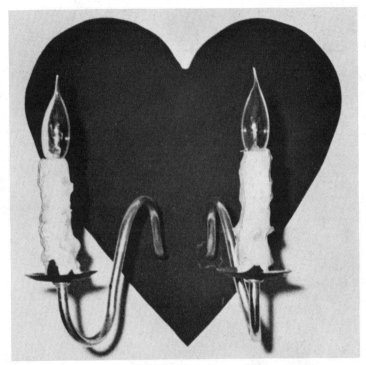

Fig. 7-10. Heart Sconce (Mr. and Mrs. Walter L. Wolfe and Antique Magazine)

Materials

Part	Pieces	Size	Suggested Materials
A — Back plate	1	14" × 18"	20-gage sheet metal
B — Arms	2	3/8" × 12"	1/8" I.P.S. brass
C — Drip dish	2	2" dia.	26-gage sheet metal
D — Sockets	2	¾" dia.	26-gage sheet metal
Electrical			
Sockets	2	¾" dia.	Adjustable candelabra
Candle covers	2	¾" × 6"	Plastic
Bulbs	2	40-watt	Flame tip®
Wire	1	36"	Lamp cord
Nuts	6	½" dia.	Decorative 1/8" I.P.S. Locknuts

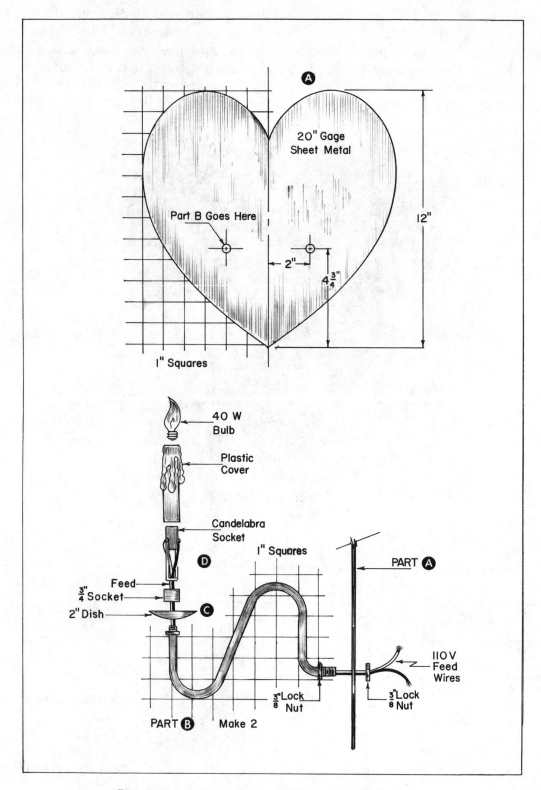

Fig. 7-11. Project Views of Friendship Wall Sconce

Construction Procedure

PART A — BACK PLATE

Lay out and cut heart shape on 20-gage sheet metal.

Drill two ⅜″ holes located as shown in Fig. 7-11.

Solder a wall hanger on the back, or drill two $\frac{3}{16}$″ holes 2 ½″ between centers if lamp is to be directly mounted on an outlet box.

PART B — ARMS

Thread both ends of the arms for ⅛″-27 IPS rod approximately 1″ deep.

Shape arms into long cyma curve on a Di-Arco® bender or similar machine.

PART C — DRIP DISH

Cut out two 2″-diameter circles and shape.

Drill a ⅜″ hole on dead center.

Solder a ¾″ sheet metal socket (Part D) over the ⅜″ hole.

PART D — METAL SOCKET

Make two ¾″ - diameter standard sockets. (See Appendix, Section I.)

Solder over center of the metal drip dishes.

ASSEMBLY

Screw IPS lock nut to end of arm which will be attached to Part A.

Insert arm through predrilled hole on Part A and secure to Part A with another lock nut. (Solder if desired.)

Insert a locknut on free end. Screw down to end of threads.

Insert predrilled drip dish (Part C) over thread arm.

Screw on an adjustable candelabra socket, locking drip dish to the candle arm.

WIRING

Feed the lamp cord through the ⅜″ brass arm from behind the plate.

Feed up through adjustable candelabra socket and secure wires to terminals.

If wall lamp is to be installed directly to an outlet box, the splice with the feed wire may be made inside the box. Use a solderless nut and tape.

If lamp is to be used without an outlet box, splice feed wire at the back of plate. Use solderless nuts and tape. Make a ⅜″ × 2″ × 2 ½″ shallow box and solder over splice.

Finish

The original sconce was bright red. Use red or flat black paint on all sheet metal work. Keep brass work bright. Drip wax over plastic candle covers and drip dishes if desired. Tole designs such as fruit or floral assortment may be used in the center.

UNIT 8

Christmaslight

Unknown in early America was the custom of decorating at Christmas time. Figure 8-1 shows present day colonial Williamsburg decked at yuletide with wreaths and garlands.

Colonial interiors in modern homes are enhanced by decorations which complement the total decor. Reproductions in this section have been developed from general colonial metalworking designs of black wrought iron scrolls which combine well with candles and holly to create a yuletide centerpiece or wall hang, Fig. 8-2.

Fig. 8-1.   Christmas Street Scene (Colonial Williamsburg)

Yule Centerpiece

Fig. 8-2. Christmas Candle Sconce

Materials

Part	Pieces	Size	Suggested Materials
A — Dish	1	6'' dia.	26-gage sheet metal
B — Legs	3	½'' × 9''	Flat band stock
C — Chimney ring	1	1'' × 9 ½''	26-gage sheet metal
D — Chimney	1	3'' dia. base	Glass
Candle socket	1	¾'' dia.	26-gage sheet metal

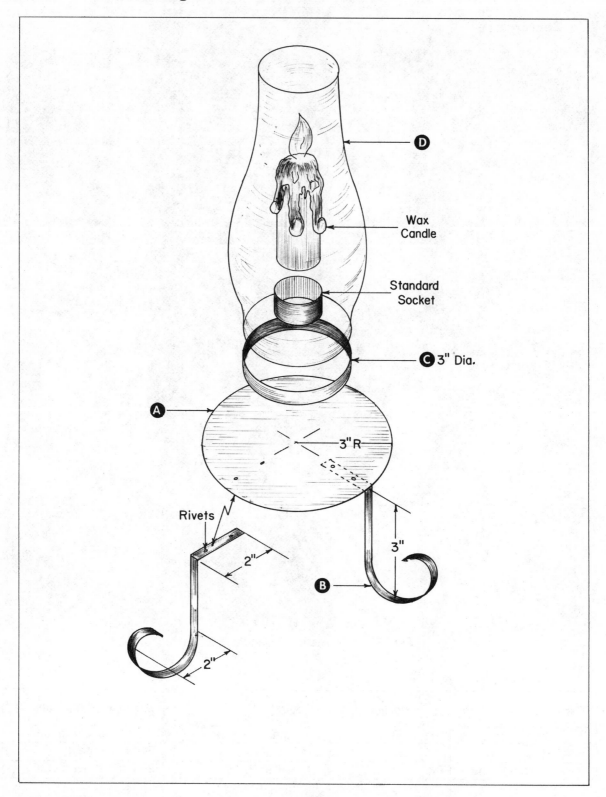

Fig. 8-3.   Project View of Colonial Christmas Centerpiece

Construction Procedure

PART A — DISH

Cut and file a 6″-diameter circle for the dish.

Divide the dish into thirds (120° sections) and drill six ⅛″ rivet holes, two for each leg as shown in Fig. 8-3.

PART B — LEGS

Cut and file ½″ flat band stock 9″ long for each of the legs.

Drill two ⅛″ rivet holes in one end of each leg, as shown. Bend to right angle 2″ from the end.

Heat and shape a cyma (double) scroll at other end.

Rivet the legs to the dish.

PART C — CHIMNEY RING

Cut and file a 1″ × 9 ½″ metal strip for the ring.

Form into 3 ⅛″-diameter circle on slip roll.

Solder joint and solder ring to center of dish.

PART D — CHIMNEY

Solder standard candle socket in center of dish, and insert glass chimney into ring. (Chimneys are available in most department or electrical stores.)

Finish

Paint the metal flat black. Use garlands of holly, pine sprays, or colored balls around edges of the dish.

Holly Wall Hang

Fig. 8-4.   Colonial Holly Wall Hang

Materials

Part	Pieces	Size	Suggested Materials
A — Wall Bracket	1	1/8'' × 1/2'' × 23''	Flat band stock
B — Dish	1	6'' dia.	26-gage sheet metal
C — Chimney ring	1	1'' × 9 1/2''	26-gage sheet metal
D — Chimney glass	1	3'' dia. base	
Candle socket	1	3/4'' dia.	26-gage sheet metal

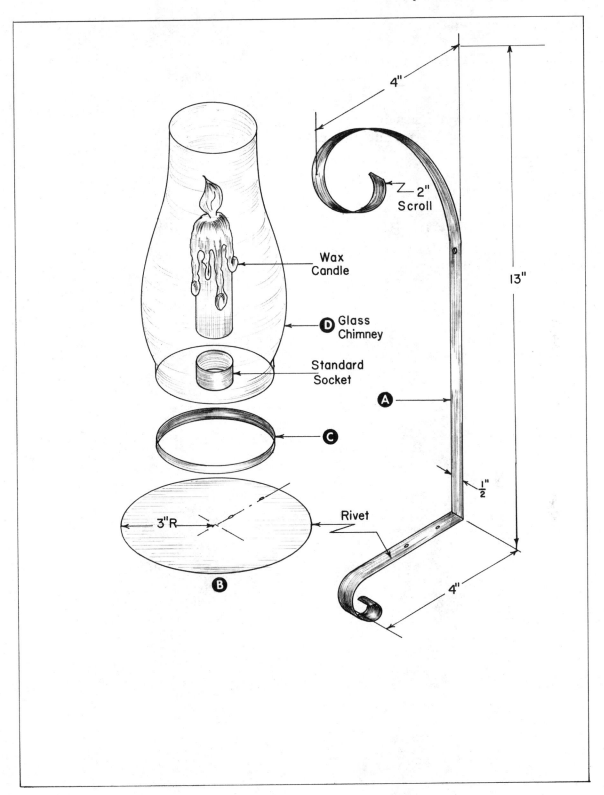

4"

2"
Scroll

Wax
Candle

D Glass
Chimney

Standard
Socket

A

13"

C

1"
2

3"R

Rivet

B

4"

Fig. 8-5.   Project View of Christmas Wall Hang

Construction Procedure

PART A — WALL BRACKET

Cut and file a ½″ × 23″ piece of flat band stock.

Drill two ⅛″ rivet holes in the bottom angle part and a ¼″ mounting hole where directed in Fig. 8-5.

Heat and shape piece according to dimensions shown.

PART B — DISH

Cut and file a circular piece of sheet metal with a 6″ diameter.

Drill two ⅛″ rivet holes for attachment to bracket, Part A.

PART C — CHIMNEY RING

Cut and file a 1″ × 9 ½″ strip of sheet metal.

Form into a 3 ⅛″ diameter circle on a slip roll.

Solder the seam and solder ring to dish, Part B.

Solder standard socket to center of dish and insert glass chimney into ring.

Insert bright-colored, 6″ candle into socket.

Finish

Paint the metal flat black. Use garland of holly, pine sprays, or miniature Christmas lights around edges of dish.

Holiday Candle Hang

Fig. 8-6.   Christmas Candle Sconce

Materials

Part	Pieces	Size	Suggested Materials
A — Cage	4	½" × 10"	1/8" flat band stock
B — Dish	1	5" dia.	26-gage sheet metal
C — Chain link	4	3/8" × 4"	1/8" flat band stock
D — Bracket	1	1" × 11"	3/16" flat band stock
E — Bracket arm	1	¼" dia. × 8"	¼" round stock
Candle	1	2" × 2" × 3"	Wax candle

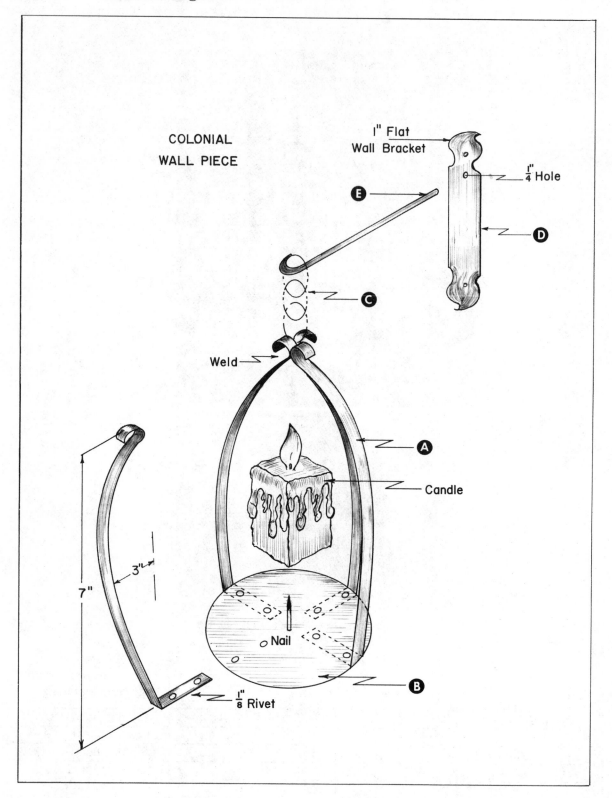

COLONIAL
WALL PIECE

1" Flat
Wall Bracket

$\frac{1}{4}$" Hole

E

D

C

Weld

A

Candle

7"

3"

Nail

B

$\frac{1}{8}$" Rivet

Fig. 8-7.   Project View of Wall Sconce

Construction Procedure

PART A — CAGE

Cut and file four pieces of ⅛″ flat band stock.

Drill two ⅛″ rivet holes in lower end of each piece as shown in Fig. 8-7.

Heat and form the basket cage. All four top scrolls should meet.

Weld the top scrolls together as shown.

PART B — DISH

Cut and file a 5″ diameter circle of sheet metal.

Drill eight ⅛″ rivet holes in dish. (Take markings from the four cage pieces.)

Solder a 6 penny nail in center to hold candle.

Rivet cage pieces to the dish.

PART C — CHAIN LINKS

Cut four pieces of flat band stock to size.

Form into circles on bench stake or slip roll. (These are open links with no fastening on the joints.)

Insert links on top of Part A.

PARTS D AND E

See construction details in ship's sconce, Page xx.

CANDLE

Make a 2″ × 2″ × 3″ wax candle by pouring melted wax into a half-pint milk carton and letting cool. (Wax may be colored by melting crayons with the wax.)

Finish

Paint the metal flat black. Colored bulbs, plastic pine sprays and holly may be added at the base of the candle.

Mass ^{TTS.} Step Piece

Fig. 8-8.   Mass ^{tts.} Step Piece for Christmas

Materials

Part	Pieces	Size	Suggested Materials
A — Base	1	1'' × 18''	3/16'' flat band stock
B — Rings	3	¼'' × 1'' dia.	Flat band or pipe
C — Base support	1	1'' × 7''	3/16'' flat band stock
Drip dishes	3	2'' dia.	26-gage sheet metal
Candle sockets	3	¾'' dia.	26-gage sheet metal

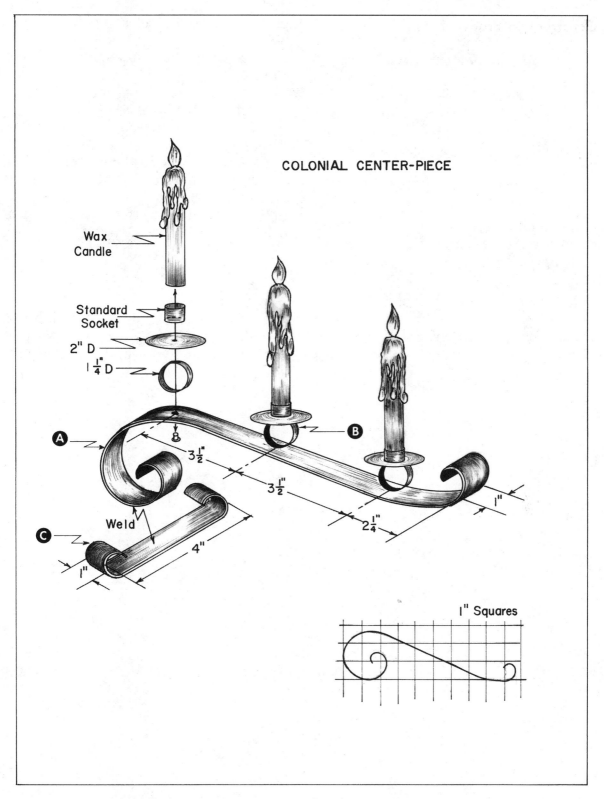

COLONIAL CENTER-PIECE

Wax Candle

Standard Socket

2" D

$1\frac{1}{4}$" D

A

B

$3\frac{1}{2}$"

$3\frac{1}{2}$"

$2\frac{1}{4}$"

1"

Weld

C

4"

1"

1" Squares

Fig. 8-9. Project View of Colonial Centerpiece

Construction Procedure

Cut and file all stock.

PART A — BASE

Heat and form the base into a large scroll as shown in Fig. 8-9.

Drill three ⅛″ rivet holes as directed.

PART B — RINGS

Heat and form rings from $\frac{3}{16}$″ flat band stock or cut off sections from 1″ diameter steel pipe.

Drill two ⅛″ rivet holes through each ring.

Rivet the rings to the base.

PART C — BASE SUPPORT

Heat and form a support base piece of 1″ flat band steel as shown in Fig. 8-9.

Weld or rivet the support to the base, Part A.

DRIP DISHES AND SOCKETS

Cut and form three 2″ diameter drip dishes.

Drill a ⅛″ hole in the center of each.

Rivet the drip dish to the top of the rings, Part B.

Solder a candle socket to the center of each dish.

Finish

Paint the entire product flat black. Use bright-colored candles with pine branches or holly around the base.

Appendix

SECTION I

Working with Metal

All the drawing dimensions have been generalized. The turns, cyma (double) curves, scrolls and points will vary from student to student — even from one piece to another because they are handmade. The turns, scrolls and curves are turned out on bench stakes, anvils, or shopmade molds, and as such it is extremely difficult to get two pieces alike, nor should they be. The reproductions were created to resemble the handmade appearance of the originals; thus every piece is different, Fig. A-1. The finished object then truly belongs to the maker an no one else.

Most often it is preferred that students create their own layouts or "stretch outs" in order to achieve a learning situation. Therefore, this procedure has been followed, only basic shapes and sizes in the working drawings being given. When individual layouts are made, you may follow the general outline yet retain the right to impose your own will and creativity upon the reproduction, thereby giving the metalwork your personal touch.

Fig. A-1.

Fig. A-2. Wrought Iron Hardware of Pennsylvania German 1700 (Philadelphia Museum of Art, Titus C. Geesey Collection.)

Forge Points

The term "forge point" merely means to "draw out" the metal into a point or decorative ending. Fig. A-2 shows some of the decorative endings on wrought iron. As a rule, the forged point is made on an anvil. The metal stock is heated to a bright red, then sharp hammer blows are delivered to the heated end. These hammer blows will slowly beat down the end of the stock. By reheating and shaping the metal, a design can be worked into the end. Fig. A-3 shows some complex designs. The (A) *fleur-de-lis* is of French origin, while the (B) tulip point is typical of Pennsylvanian art. Other points are shown in Figs. 2-10 and 2-11.

In order to speed up forge shaping, some of the excess stock may be cut off first. Fig. A-4 shows how excess metal is cut away with a hacksaw or chisel for the strap hinge sconce. The stock is heated and hammered to a finished shape.

Colonial Points

Shaping points on the reproductions gives them authenticity and avoids the "squared off" look of most manufactured metal projects. Fig. 1-2 shows some of the most common colonial shapes used on hardware in the 1700's. Pointing heat can be achieved by using a small "copper" furnace, forge, Fig. A-5, or even a charcoal furnace. Pointing is a basic necessity for all wrought iron projects.

Scroll Work

A scroll is much like a loose clock spring, having a constantly increasing

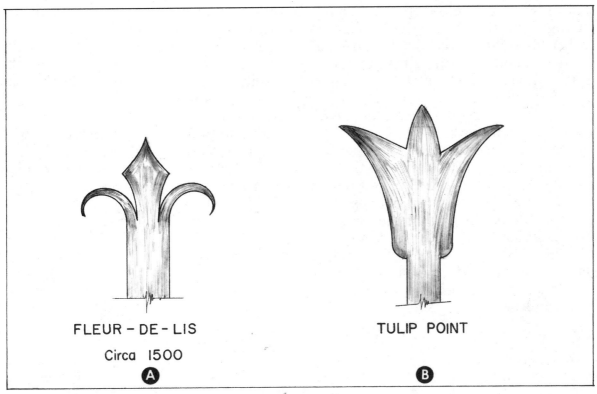

FLEUR – DE – LIS

Circa 1500

Ⓐ

TULIP POINT

Ⓑ

Fig. A-3.   Forge points shown are the (A) fleur-de-Lis and (B) tulip.

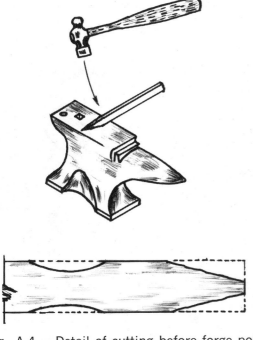

Fig. A-4.   Detail of cutting before forge point-ing.

Fig. A-5.   Forge Furnace

radius. Simple scroll shapes are shown in Fig. A-6. Scrolls may be shaped on a bench stake, anvil horn, DiAcro® bender, metal former, or bending fork. Fig. A-7 shows how a scroll is made on a DiArco® bender and Fig. A-8 shows some of the many bench stakes available for scroll work.

The total finished scroll shape should be in harmony with the size of the material and project. Sizes suggested in the drawings serve as guidelines. Balance should be the guiding factor in all scrollmaking. If the stock is thin and of a light gage, then the scroll should be small and tight; if the stock is very heavy and thick, then the scroll can be loose and large.

Cyma Curves

The *cyma* curve is basically a double curve formed by the union of concave and convex lines. Early Greeks used this curve, called a "classic" design. The colonists used the cyma curve extensively in metal work and in woodworking. Many arms, stems, or extended pieces in the reproductions are shaped into cyma curves, giving the pieces colonial authenticity and enhancing the overall design. Fig. A-9 shows the use of a cyma curve in the balance arm of the scale and in the arm of a chandelier.

CONSTRUCTION

A full-size drawing will be very helpful. Lay out the size desired and construct the curves, using a "French curve." Heat the metal stock and form the curve over a bench stake or anvil horn, checking the stock against the full-size drawing frequently to insure faithful reproduction. Reheating will be necessary for slight adjustments.

Holes should be drilled after the scrolls or curves are formed because no two curves or scrolls will be the same. It is extremely difficult to mark off high points before forming the curves, but after the scrolls or curves are made, it is a simple task to find the high points and drill the stock.

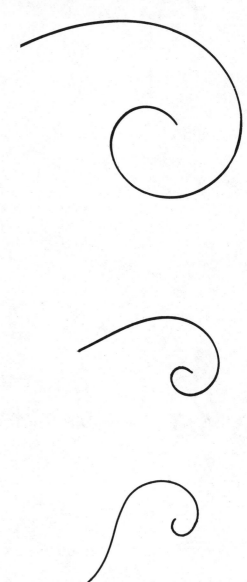

Fig. A-6.   Simple Scroll Shapes

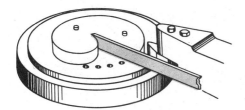

Adjust Forming Nose so material will fit snugly between Nose and "high point" of contour collar and insert material as shown.

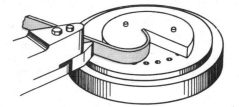

Advance Operating Arm with a steady even pressure. Note how material bends only where resistance is offered by contour collar.

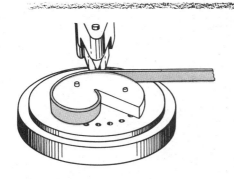

Material continues to bend and take shape of contour collar as Operating Arm is advanced.

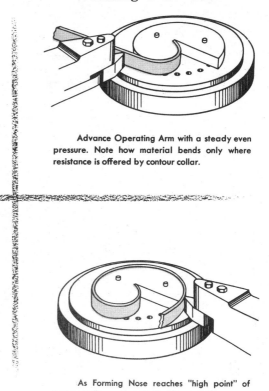

As Forming Nose reaches "high point" of contour collar, material is "set" in new shape.

Fig. A-7. Making a scroll on a DiAcro® bender. (DiAcro Corp.)

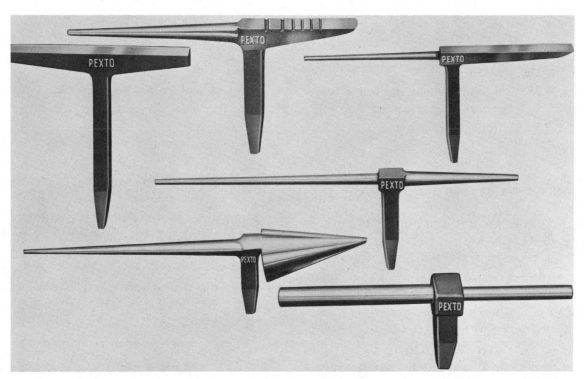

Fig. A-8. Bench stakes. For scroll work the "blow horn" stake works best. (Pexto Corp.)

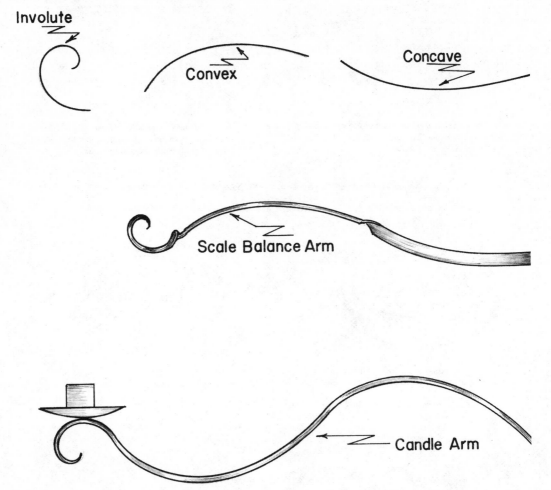

Fig. A-9.   The basic parts of a "cyma" curve are shown at top. Lower drawings show how this curve was worked into the balance arm for the scale and a candle arm for a Raleigh chandelier.

Hammer Marks

Hammer marks will not detract from the finished project. They should not be too deep or uniform but, in general, resemble the distressing in colonial wood furniture. These handwrought marks create a surface texture comparable to original colonial pieces. In contrast, modern machine - produced wrought iron often has a slick or overly smooth texture.

Candle Sockets and Drip Dishes

Most of the candleholder projects require a socket (holder) and a drip dish. The socket holds the candle, while the dish prevents dripping wax from falling on floors or furniture. These items are of simple design and are used for both wax candles or electric candles.

SOCKET CONSTRUCTION

The average candle socket is made from a strip of 26 or 28-gage sheet metal, 3 $\frac{1}{8}$" long × $\frac{3}{4}$" or 1" wide. A $\frac{3}{16}$" hem is put on the ends to make a simple lock seam.

Rough-bend the sheet stock around a bench stake and complete the seam lock. Hammer the seam tight and solder. After the seam is secure, give the candle socket a finished round shape on the stake. Fig. A-10 shows how to make the seam and final shape.

This candle socket will serve the average candle which has a base of $\frac{5}{8}$" or $\frac{3}{4}$". However, if larger candles are to be used, the socket must be made larger.

DRIP DISH CONSTRUCTION

The drip dish may be cut from scrap 26 or 28-gage sheet stock. The dish is cut in a circle and then given a concave shape by using a wood mold or by the peen end of a hammer on a sand bag, Fig. A-11. The depth of the dish depends on the individual's choice; however, a $\frac{1}{4}$" or $\frac{3}{8}$" concave is considered adequate for any of the reproductions. Diameter of the dish depends upon the overall size of the finished project and the size of stock used. Sizes are suggested. A sense of balance is the best rule to follow.

FASTENING

Fastening sheet metal to strap stock represents somewhat of a problem. Drill or punch a $\frac{1}{8}$" rivet hole in the center of the dish. Rivet the dish to the strap metal. Solder a premade candle socket to the center of the concave side of the dish. The finished socket and candle will cover the rivet head.

Joints and Seams

The early craftsmen did not seek invisible joints in their work. Rivets and solder joints were smooth and very neat but otherwise not concealed. The rivets used in the majority of the reproductions are $\frac{1}{8}$", $\frac{3}{16}$" or $\frac{1}{4}$" roundhead, soft steel rivets. The $\frac{1}{4}$" roundhead rivets are used mainly to give a heavy effect. The strap hinge sconce, Fig. 2-11, is a good example of riveting for effect. Rivets used in the reproductions closely resemble the handmade rivets of early blacksmiths, whitesmiths and tinkers. The welds called for in the projects should be as small and neatly made as possible. Colonials used a process called forge welding which resembles modern arc welding. Spot welding should be avoided if at all possible.

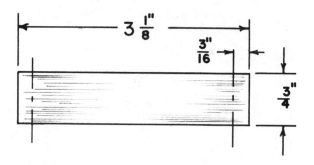

Finished Socket

Fig. A-10. Standard metal socket detail.

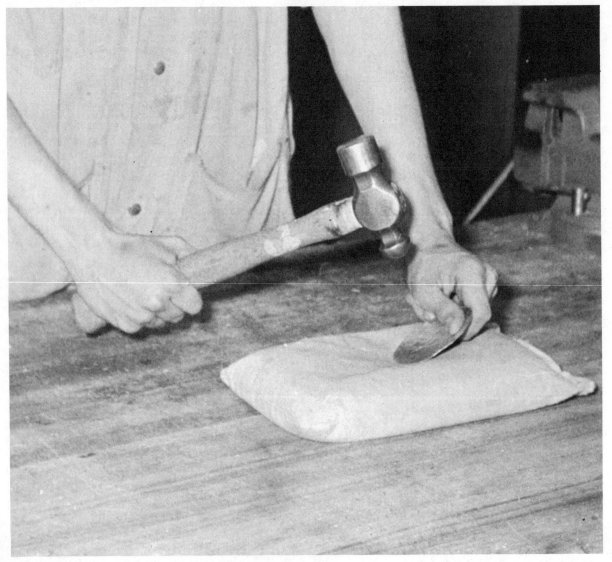

Fig. A-11. The drip dish is hammered into shape on a sand bag.

Electric Candle Sockets

The electric socket used in the re-productions is an adjustable-height, threaded base (27-⅛″ IPS) candelabra socket which will take a 40-watt candle flame bulb. This electrical unit fits in-side the standard sheet metal socket. Fig. A-12 and A-13 show two common candelabra types of electric sockets. The threaded base will fit on standard ⅛″ IPS threaded rod or nipple. Plastic covers in 4 or 6-inch size are placed over sockets and melted wax dripped on the cover so the effect is that of a wax candle. How this type of candel-abra socket is assembled is shown in Fig. 7-6. (If you have trouble securing these items in your area, check Section III of the Appendix for a list of nation-wide suppliers.)

Fig. A-12. Adjustable height electric candelabra socket. (Circle F, Inc.)

Fig. A-13. Plain candelabra electric socket.

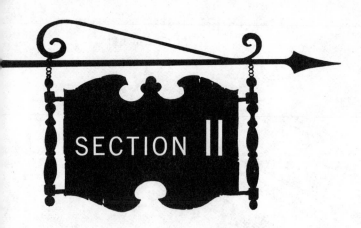

SECTION II

Metal Finishes and Design

The type and extent of finishes is somewhat limited on colonial metal-work. In general, finishes are needed for protection, appearance, and identification. Most wrought iron and sheet-metal projects have a tendency to be flat black. This, of course, is a heritage from colonial times. Most wrought iron was colored by heating the stock until a temper color was achieved and then the stock was plunged into water. Today, the majority of wrought iron work has a flat black finish. The type of finish for each project is designated in the text.

Preparing Metal

Most shops use a galvanized sheet-metal stock. While this zinc coat helps protect the base metal from rusting, it also prevents the good adherence of oil-based paints. Several methods can be used to "cut" this zinc coat. Household vinegar will work on small projects. However, an automotive body product with a phosphoric acid base will do the work much quicker and achieve a better cutting action. This product is sold under several trade names and is available at most automotive or paint supply outlets. Even though it is an acid cut with water, care must be taken in its use. Follow the directions given on the containers for best results.

DEGREASER

A degreaser is also a prerequisite for proper finishing. For small work, a wash coat of thinner or turpentine will serve the purpose, or a good commercial degreaser can be used. In all cases, proper care and safety precautions must be followed.

After using a zinc cutter or degreaser, the project must be washed clean. After washing, force-dry the project and prime as soon as possible since oxidation starts immediately and will hinder perfect finishing results. Projects can be ruined when these important steps are not observed in the finishing operations.

Painted Surfaces

On new metal the best results are achieved by using a primer. Any good zinc chromate primer will do. Allow at least 24 hours for drying, then cover with one or two coats of the finish paint. If exterior wear is desired, use a commercial primer, followed by one or two coats of exterior paint. Several companies produce exterior metal paints in flat black or in colors. Follow the manufacturer's instructions closely.

Aged-Effect Finishes

Several paint manufacturers now offer small pressure spray cans of finishes in colonial or aged-effect colors. Pewter tone, Old English bronze and aged copper are only a few. Prepare the metal in the normal manner and then spray two or three light coats of the desired finish. Shake the spray can for a prolonged period before using and shake periodically while using to achieve a uniform result. Use a fanlike sweeping motion, and allow plenty of drying time in between coats.

Natural Finish

Wrought iron created from hot-rolled stock has a pleasing dull grey, natural color. On several projects, especially the strap hinge sconce or wrought iron hanging lamps, this natural color was highlighted by the following method:

1. Wire brush the entire surface, using a fine wire brush in an electric hand drill or drill press.
2. Steel wool the surface to bring out a satin sheen.
3. Coat the project with a brushing lacquer. This will produce a high sheen which can be mellowed by using a paste wax. Do not use this finish for exterior work.

Trim and Design

Colored trim or motif enhances many projects. Several candle sconces are decorated with a colonial eagle, flowers,

Fig. A-14. Plank wood walls are stenciled with American eagles and floral designs CA 1800. (Shelburne Museum)

Fig. A-15. This carved wood eagle is a suitable subject for a tracing to be used in decorating reproductions. (Shelburne Museum)

or Dutch colonial border. Fig. A-14 illustrates the use of stenciled decoration. Color brightens the large areas of flat black and is particularly suitable to contemporary colonial decor. While several lacquer colors are available, these require a lacquer base and some skill in application. However, regular oil colors will achieve the desired results at small cost and with only a little painting skill. Using artist's brushes, most students can paint by the numbers inside given guidelines. Numerous motifs such as eagles (see Fig. A-15), flowers, birds or other colonial-type decorations are available in newspapers, magazines and books. Enlargements or reductions may be necessary but these motifs can be transferred to the project without any difficulty. Hand paint within the guidelines and you will achieve a handsome effect.

Decals

Several decal companies now produce colonial eagles in gold or natural colors, Dutch colonial flowers and birds and other designs in bright colors. These decals are inexpensive and applied easily to any metal surface, see Figs. 2-6 and 2-7. Most department or hardware stores carry a complete line of these decals. Other suppliers are listed in Section III of the Appendix.

Lettering

Some projects call for hand lettering for which decals or pressure-sensitive lettering may be used. Many art books have stylized alphabets from which a master copy may be made. Old English lettering works very well for most colonial reproductions.

SECTION III

Suppliers

Metal Stock

Steel shapes listed below can be purchased from steel supply outlets in the larger cities or from school supply companies. All metal items used in this text are considered standard stock items.

Following are some of the common sizes of metal stock used in most of the reproductions. Only the andirons require a special size.

FLATS
$1'' \times \frac{3}{16}''$, $\frac{1}{2}'' \times \frac{5}{8}''$, $\frac{1}{8}'' \times \frac{3}{8}''$

ROUNDS
$\frac{1}{4}''$, $\frac{3}{8}''$, $\frac{1}{2}''$ and some $1''$ hot-rolled diameters. $\frac{3}{4}''$ or $15/16''$ diameters of brass.

SHEET STOCK
28, 26, 24, and 20 or 18-gage sheet metal. (22-gage sheet brass, pewter, bronze or copper is available if desired).

SPECIAL STOCK
28-gage tin plate, 24-gage half-hard brass, and $2'' \times \frac{3}{8}''$ steel bar for the andirons.

NOTE: At times steel bars or rods can be found in local junk yards at a reduced rate. Many supply outlets will sell steel bars and rods in short lengths at scrap prices.

Fasteners

Soldering, rivets, and some machine screws will suffice for all of the projects. A good tap and die set is required for construction of several projects. However, if you lack a complete set you may obtain the most desirable sizes such as the $\frac{1}{4}''$ and $\frac{3}{8}''$ national course and national fine, through your school shop or at most hardware stores.

Electrical Equipment

Most cities have several electrical supply outlets from which the various types of electrical sockets, plastic covers, and decorative bulbs needed in some of the projects can be obtained. The adjustable candelabra sockets and 40 or 25-watt Flame Tip® bulbs are inpensive. Because these sockets have expensive. Because these sockets have different characteristics imposed by different manufacturers, it would be wise to have the material on hand so that adjustments in construction and

144

fastening methods can be made during the planning stage of the project. Chandelier chain, ceiling outlet covers, and lamp cord can be purchased in local electric or hardware stores.

If purchasing these parts is difficult, order direct from the manufacturer.

Electrical Suppliers

Circle F Corporation, Trenton, N.J. —sockets and candelabra bulbs

Gyro Electric Corporation, 5208 N.W. 35th Ave., Miami, Fla. 33142 —electrical fixtures and parts

North American Electric Lamp Company, 1520 N. 13th St., St. Louis, Mo. 63106 — drip wax candle covers

Old Guilford Forge, Guilford, Conn. 06437 — candelabra bulbs

Sears, Roebuck & Co., local store or catalog — chandelier chain, electric sockets, bulbs

Sturbridge Yankee Workshop, Brimfield Turnpike, Sturbridge, Mass. 01566 — bulbs and sockets

Decal Suppliers

Try local paint, department, hardware or art stores first.

Authentic Decals, Box 43158, Cincinnati, O. 45243

Old Guilford Forge, Guilford, Conn. 06437

Sturbridge Yankee Workshop, Brimfield Turnpike, Sturbridge, Mass. 01566

Sears, Roebuck & Co., local store or catalog